How to use the handbook

How to use the handbook

This handbook contains nearly 1500 words used in physics. These are arranged in groups under the main headings listed on p. 3. The entries are grouped according to the meaning of the words to help the reader to obtain a broad understanding of the subject.

At the top of each page the subject is shown in bold type and the part of the subject in lighter type. For example, on pp. 92 and 93:

92 · ELECTRICITY & MAGNETISM/PERMANENT MAGNETS
ELECTRICITY & MAGNETISM/MAGNETIC MATERIALS · **93**

In the definitions, the words used have been limited so far as possible to about 1500 words that are in common use, taken from the *New Method English Dictionary* (fifth edition) by M. West and J. G. Endicott (Longman 1976).

1. To find the meaning of a word

Look for the word in the alphabetical index at the end of the book, then turn to the page number listed.

In the index you may find words with a number at the end. These only occur where the same word appears more than once in the handbook in different contexts. For example, **pole**.

$pole^1$ is the centre of a curved mirror

$pole^2$ is the area on a magnet where flux lines enter or leave

The description of the word may contain some words with arrows in brackets (parentheses) after them. This shows that the words with arrows are defined nearby.

(↑) means the related word appears above or on the facing page;

(↓) means the related word appears below or on the facing page.

A word with a page number in brackets after it is defined elsewhere in the handbook on the page indicated. Looking up the words referred to may help in understanding the meaning of the word being defined.

In some cases more than one meaning is given for the same word. Where this is so, the first definition given is the more (or most) common usage of the word. At the end of the definitions, you will find listed any symbols and alternative terms (also known as . . .).

The explanation of each word usually depends on knowing the meaning of a word or words above it. For example, on p. 158 the meaning of *radioisotope, daughter nuclide, a-particle*, and the words that follow, depends on the meaning of *radioactive* which appears above them. Once the earlier words have been read, those that follow become easier to understand. The illustrations have been designed to help the reader understand the definitions, but the definitions are not dependent on the illustrations.

2. To find related words

Look at the index for the word you are starting from and turn to the page number shown. Because this handbook is arranged by ideas, related words will be found in a group on that page or one nearby. The illustrations will also help to show how the words relate to one another.

For example, words relating to the electromagnetic spectrum are on pp. 86–89. On p. 86 *electromagnetic spectrum* and *radio wave* are followed by definitions of *long wave*, *medium wave* and *short wave*; on p. 87 *very high frequency* and *ultra high frequency* are defined; and the section then defines and illustrates words related to *radar*, *microwaves*, *infra-red* and *ultra-violet waves*, and *X-rays*.

3. As an aid to studying or revising

The handbook can be used for studying or revising a topic. For example, to revise your knowledge of semiconductors, you would look up *semiconductor* in the alphabetical index. Turning to the page indicated, p. 132, you would find *semiconductor* and *n-type semiconductor*; on the next page you would find *p-type semiconductor*, *acceptor atom*, *hole*, and so on; on the following page you would find *pn junction*, *depletion layer*, *semiconductor diode*, etc.

In this way, starting with one word in a topic you can revise all the words that are important to this topic.

4. To find a word to fit a required meaning

It is almost impossible to find a word to fit a meaning in most books, but easy with this handbook. For example, if you had forgotten the word for a negatively charged electrode, all you would have to do would be to look up *electrode* in the alphabetical index and turn to the page indicated, p.113. There you would find the word *cathode*.

5. Abbreviations used in the definitions

abbr	abbreviated as	n	noun
adj	adjective	p.	page
e.g.	*exempli gratia*	pl	plural
	(for example)	pp.	pages
etc	*et cetera* (and so on)	sing.	singular
i.e.	*id est* (that is	v	verb
	to say)	=	the same as

THE
HANDBOOK

Système International the system of units (↓) which has been chosen for use in all physics around the world. If all the quantities put into a calculation are measured in SI units (↓), the result will also be in the correct SI unit. Also known as the **metric system**. **SI** (*abbr*).

metric system = Système International (↑).

unit (*n*) the quantity of a measurement; e.g. all distances can be measured as a number of metres.

SI unit a unit (↑) which is used for a quantity in the Système International (↑).

base unit a unit (↑) which is chosen in a special way and is one of the fundamental (p.238) units of the Système International (↑); e.g. the units of mass, length, time.

derived unit a unit (↑) which can be described in terms of the base units (↑) of the Système International (↑); e.g. the unit of velocity (p.10) in the Système International is the metre per second, which is measured from the base units for length and time.

inertia

inertia of cups makes them stay on table when cloth pulled away

prefix (*n*) a word placed before the name of a unit (↑), which changes the size of the unit; e.g. kilo- . A kilometre is 1000 metre, a kilowatt is 1000 watt; so kilo- has the effect of multiplying the size of the unit by 1000.

mass (*n*) a measure of how much material an object contains, and thus of how much force will be needed to make it move in a certain way. The mass of an object depends only on what it is and not on where the object is, e.g. it does not depend on the strength of gravity (p.23) acting on the object. If the special theory of relativity (p.34) is taken into account, the mass of an object also depends on how fast it is moving. **massive** (*adj*).

inertia (*n*) the property which an object has because of its mass. An object which has more mass is harder to make move; it thus has more inertia.

kilogram (*n*) the SI unit (↑) of mass. It is the mass of a particular piece of platinum-iridium alloy (p.236) that is kept at Sèvres, France. It is about equal to the mass of 1dm³ of water at 4°C. **kg** (*abbr*).

international prototype kilogram a particular piece of platinum-iridium alloy (p.236) kept at Sèvres, France, the mass of which is chosen to be one kilogram (↑).

length (*n*) the distance from one end of an object to the other.

metre (*n*) the SI unit (↑) of length (↑). It is the distance travelled by light in a vacuum in a time of 1/299 792 458 s.

second (*n*) the SI unit (↑) of time. It is the time that is taken for 9 192 631 770 periods (p.36) of the electromagnetic wave (p.59) in a particular line in the emission spectrum (p.81) of caesium-133.

balance (*n*) an instrument for measuring mass, by comparing the force of gravity (p.23) on an unknown mass against the force on a known mass.

metre rule a simple instrument for measuring length (↑). It is made of a straight piece of solid material, one metre long, with marks on it showing each millimetre.

micrometer screw gauge an instrument which is used for measuring small distances, usually to the nearest 0.01mm. The object to be measured is put between two flat metal faces on the micrometer screw gauge: one face is fixed, the other moves on a screw thread. The thread is made in such a way that the moving face moves forward 0.5mm for each turn of the screw, and the edge of the screw has a scale which measures how far it has turned, with fifty marks to a turn. The position of the moving face can thus be found with this degree of accuracy. Also known as a **micrometer**.

micrometer (*n*) = micrometer screw gauge (↑).

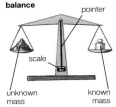

balance

pointer

scale

unknown mass

known mass

micrometer screw gauge

speed

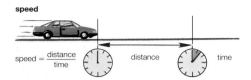

$\text{speed} = \dfrac{\text{distance}}{\text{time}}$ distance   time

velocity

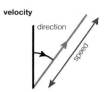

direction

speed

vector

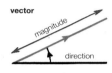

magnitude

direction

speed (*n*) the distance travelled by an object divided by the time taken to travel the distance. If the speed to be measured is changing, the time over which the speed is measured should be small, otherwise an average speed is found, rather than the speed at one moment. SI unit (p.8): metre per second.

velocity (*n*) the speed (↑) of an object together with its direction of motion. Velocity is a vector (↓), while speed is a scalar (↓). SI unit (p.8): metre per second.

scalar (*n*) a quantity which does not have a direction; e.g. mass, temperature (p.181).

vector (*n*) a quantity which has a direction, e.g. force.

magnitude (*n*) the scalar (↑) part of a vector (↑), i.e. its size without any information about its direction.

ticker-timer

wires to a.c. supply   carbon paper   magnet

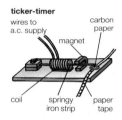

coil   springy iron strip   paper tape

ticker-timer (*n*) a simple instrument which is used for measuring speed. A point makes marks on a strip of paper, through carbon paper, at fixed periods of time. The point is fixed to a springy iron bar which passes between the poles (p.90) of a permanent magnet (p.91), and through a solenoid (p.114) which is connected to an a.c. (p.125) supply. The two magnetic fields (p.92) cause the bar to oscillate (p.35) up and down with a frequency (p.36) equal to that of the a.c. supply, making marks separated in time by the period (p.36) of the a.c.

stroboscope

wheel with equally spaced slits

viewing slit

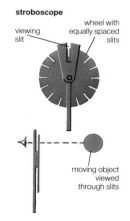

moving object viewed through slits

stroboscope (*n*) an instrument which is used for studying motion. It shows a series of short views of the system that is being studied. This is done by using a light which gives short flashes of light at fixed times, so the system is in darkness the rest of the time, or by looking at the system through a turning wheel with one or more holes in it.

stroboscopic photograph

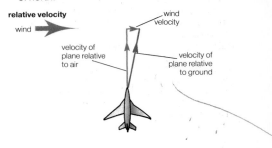

velocity-time graph

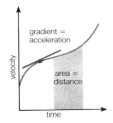

distance-time graph

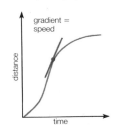

stroboscopic photograph a photograph which is taken through, or with the light from, a stroboscope (↑). Objects which move are seen on the photograph as a series of clear pictures. The distance from one picture to the next can be measured, and as the time from one picture to the next is known, the speed of the motion can be found.

velocity-time graph a graph of velocity (↑) against time. On the graph, motion with fixed velocity is shown as a horizontal line. The gradient (slope) of the line on the graph is equal to the acceleration (p.12) in the motion, and the area under the line is equal to the distance travelled in the motion.

distance-time graph a graph of distance against time. On the graph, motion with fixed velocity (↑) is a straight line, and the gradient (slope) of the line is equal to the speed.

relative velocity the velocity (↑) of one moving object as seen from another; e.g. if an aeroplane flies north at 250 m/s through air which is blowing to the east at 50 m/s, the velocity of the aeroplane relative to the air is north at 250 m/s, but the velocity of the aeroplane relative to the ground is 255 m/s at an angle of 11 degrees east of north.

relative velocity

acceleration

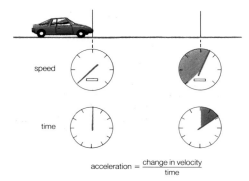

$$\text{acceleration} = \frac{\text{change in velocity}}{\text{time}}$$

acceleration (*n*) a measure of how quickly velocity (p.10) changes; the change in velocity in a given time divided by the time taken for the velocity change. If the acceleration is changing, the time over which change is measured must be small or else an average acceleration will be found. Acceleration is given by the gradient (slope) of a line on a velocity-time graph (p.11). Note that it is changes in velocity that are used, not changes in speed (p.10), so motion in a circle may be at constant speed, but still has an acceleration. SI unit (p.8): metre per second squared (or metre per second per second). **accelerate** (*v*).

acceleration due to gravity the acceleration (↑) with which all objects fall when the only force on them is gravity (p.23). This acceleration is the same for all objects at a given place, and can be used as a measure of the strength of gravity at that place. On Earth the acceleration due to gravity is about 9.8 m/s^2.

strength of gravity the force of gravity (p.23) on each kilogram of material present. The strength of gravity in newtons per kilogram is equal to the acceleration due to gravity in metres per second squared. SI unit (p.8): newton (p.14) per kilogram.

acceleration due to gravity

to vacuum pump

glass tube

in a vacuum, coin and feather fall with same acceleration

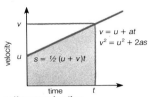

velocity

$v = u + at$
$v^2 = u^2 + 2as$
$s = \frac{1}{2}(u + v)t$

time t

uniform acceleration

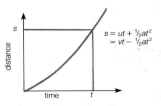

distance

$s = ut + \frac{1}{2}at^2$
$= vt - \frac{1}{2}at^2$

time t

equations for motion with uniform acceleration where an object moves with uniform (p.239) acceleration (↑) a, starting at velocity (p.10) u, finishing at velocity v, travelling a distance s in a time t, the equations are:
$$v = u + at$$
$$s = ut + \frac{1}{2}at^2$$
$$v^2 = u^2 + 2as$$
$$s = \frac{1}{2}(u + v)t$$
$$s = vt - \frac{1}{2}at^2.$$

free fall motion in which the only force causing acceleration (↑) is gravity (p.23).

projectile

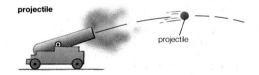

projectile

projectile (*n*) an object which is given a starting velocity (p.10), usually at an angle to the ground, and then left to move with gravity (p.23) and air resistance (p.32) as the only forces acting on it. If air resistance is small enough to be neglected (p.238), the projectile will move in a parabolic (p.234) curve.

range (*n*) the distance a projectile (↑) travels before hitting the ground. This will be largest when the projectile starts by moving at an angle of 45° to the ground.

equation of motion an equation from which the motion of an object can be found. Usually the starting position and velocity (p.10) must be known, together with the force on the object at each point in its motion.

force (*n*) a push or a pull that, when it acts on an object, tends to cause the object to accelerate (p.12).

newton (*n*) the SI unit (p.8) of force; a force of one newton will cause a mass of one kilogram to accelerate (p.12) at one metre per second squared. **N** (*abbr*).

contact force a force on two objects which can act only when there is no space between them; e.g. friction (↓). Contact forces are a result of forces between the atoms (p.139) in the surfaces of the two objects.

Newton's first law an object will remain at rest or continue to move at a steady speed (p.10) in a straight line if it is not acted on by an external force (↓).

external force a force which acts on a system from the outside so that its effect is not destroyed by an opposite force produced according to Newton's third law (↓).

Newton's second law the rate of change (p.235) of momentum (p.21) is proportional (p.235) to the force acting. If the mass of the system does not change, this means that the force is proportional to the mass multiplied by the acceleration (p.12). In SI units (p.8), the constant of proportionality (p.235) is taken as one, so the force is *equal to* the rate of change of momentum.

Newton's third law when one object causes a force on another, the second object produces an equal but opposite force on the first. Newton's third law is sometimes written as 'for every action (↓) there is an equal and opposite reaction (↓)'. It is important to remember that action and reaction forces act on different objects.

action (*n*) one of the pair of forces in Newton's third law (↑). It is equal and opposite to the reaction (↓) and acts on a different object from the reaction.

reaction (*n*) one of the pair of forces in Newton's third law (↑). It is equal and opposite to the action (↑) and acts on a different object from the action.

Newton's third law

normal reaction

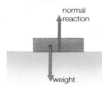

normal reaction the part of the contact force (↑) between two flat surfaces which is at 90° to the surfaces.

friction (*n*) the part of the contact force (↑) between two surfaces which is parallel to the surfaces. It is the result of attraction (p.239) between the atoms (p.139) of the two surfaces and is what stops them sliding freely over each other. Friction is increased by increasing the normal reaction (↑) between the two surfaces, and by using rough surfaces. It is also sometimes very large with extremely smooth flat surfaces. **frictional** (*adj*).

friction

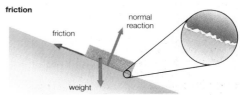

static friction friction (↑) between two surfaces which are not sliding over each other, but which would slide over each other if there was no friction.

limiting friction

block does not slide

block just about to slide

block accelerates down slope

dynamic friction friction (↑) between two surfaces which are sliding over each other. Dynamic friction is usually a little less than the maximum static friction (↑), so once an object starts to slide, it will often continue to do so.

limiting friction the largest value that the force of friction (↑) can take in a given system.

coefficient of friction the limiting friction (↑) or the dynamic friction (↑) divided by the normal reaction (↑).

coefficient of friction

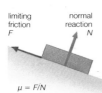

$\mu = F/N$

angle of friction

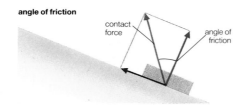

contact force

angle of friction

angle of friction the angle between the contact force (p.14) and the normal (p.234) to the surfaces, when the friction (p.15) is the limiting friction (p.15).

equilibrium (*n*) the state of a system where nothing is changing, particularly the state of a system where all the forces on the system add up to zero, and the moments (p.19) of these forces about any point also add up to zero, so the system will not accelerate (p.12).

stable equilibrium an equilibrium (↑) where a small change in the state of the system produces forces that will try to return the system to its equilibrium position.

unstable equilibrium an equilibrium (↑) where a small change in the state of the system produces forces that will try to move the system away from its equilibrium position.

neutral equilibrium an equilibrium (↑) where a small change in the state of the system will not produce any forces on the system.

metastable equilibrium an equilibrium (↑) where a very small change in the state of the system will produce forces that try to return the system to its equilibrium position, but where larger changes in the state of the system will produce forces which try to move it away from its equilibrium position.

static equilibrium an equilibrium (↑) where nothing is moving.

dynamic equilibrium an equilibrium (↑) where parts of a system may not be in equilibrium even though the system as a whole is; e.g. a molecule (p.188) in an object will not be in equilibrium at all times even if there are no external forces (p.14) acting on the object.

stable equilibrium

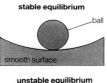

ball

smooth surface

unstable equilibrium

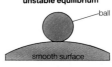

ball

smooth surface

neutral equilibrium

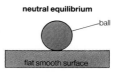

ball

flat smooth surface

metastable equilibrium

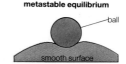

ball

smooth surface

work

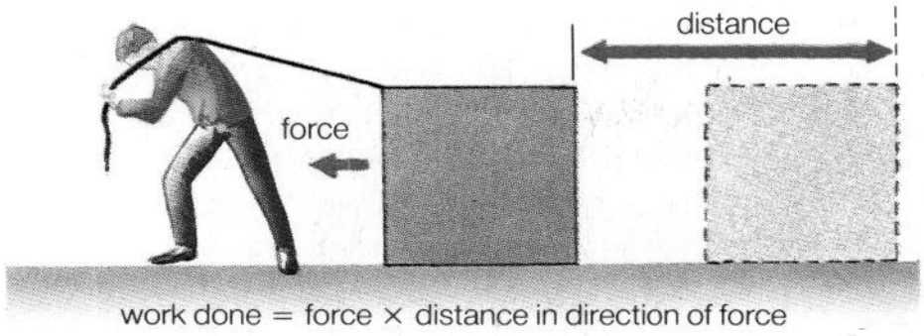

work done = force × distance in direction of force

work (*n*) the energy which is used or produced
when a force moves over a distance, or when
energy (↓) is changed from one form to another.
The amount of work done is equal to the force
times the distance moved in the direction of the
force. Note that no work is done if the direction of
motion is at 90° to the direction of the force.

joule (*n*) the SI unit (p.8) of work (↑); one joule of
work is done when a force of one newton
(p.14) moves through a distance of one metre.
J (*abbr*).

energy (*n*) the ability to do work. If something is
able to do work on something else, it has energy.
Energy can be divided into two main types:
kinetic energy (p.18) and potential energy (↓). SI
unit (p.8): joule (↑).

potential energy the energy that a system has
because of its position or state. **p.e.** (*abbr*).

chemical energy the energy stored in bonds
(p.221) between atoms (p.139), which can be
released in a chemical reaction (p.236).
Chemical energy is a form of potential energy (↑).

potential energy

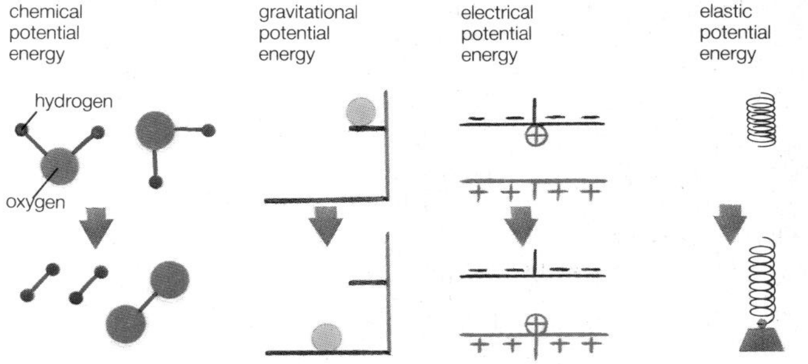

chemical
potential
energy

gravitational
potential
energy

electrical
potential
energy

elastic
potential
energy

hydrogen

oxygen

gravitational potential energy the energy which
an object has from its position in a gravitational
field (p.24). This can be released by allowing the
object to fall to a lower height, where it will have
less gravitational potential energy. The change in
gravitational potential energy caused by
changing the height of an object of mass m by a
distance h is mgh, where g is the strength of
gravity (p.23). **g.p.e.** (*abbr*).

electrical potential energy the energy of a
charge (p.95) in an electric field (p.97).

elastic potential energy[1] the energy an object
has because it is stretched or compressed
(p.214). The object will release energy when it is
allowed to return to its usual size.

kinetic energy the energy an object has from its
motion. An object of mass m moving with a
speed v will have kinetic energy $\frac{1}{2}mv^2$. **k.e.**
(*abbr*).

heat energy the energy an object has if it is hot.
Since heating something makes its molecules
(p.188) move faster, heat energy is a form of
kinetic energy (↑). It is internal energy (p.204)
rather than energy caused by all the molecules in
the object moving in the same direction.

thermal energy = heat energy (↑).

mechanical energy the energy an object has in
the form of kinetic energy (↑), or gravitational
potential energy (↑) or elastic potential energy (↑).

law of conservation of energy energy can never
be created or destroyed, but only changed from
one form to another.

equivalence of mass and energy according to
the special theory of relativity (p.34), mass and
energy are closely related. An object that has
more energy will have more mass, and when
mass is destroyed, other forms of energy will be
released. E.g. objects which are moving at a
speed quite close to the speed of light (p.59)
gain mass. When a nucleus (p.139) is formed it
has a mass less than the mass of the protons
(p.155) and neutrons (p.155) from which it is
made. The relationship between energy and
mass is shown by $E = mc^2$, where E is the
energy, m the mass, and c the speed of light.

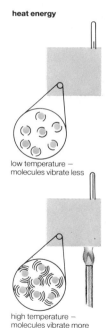

heat energy

low temperature –
molecules vibrate less

high temperature –
molecules vibrate more

lever

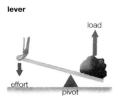

moment

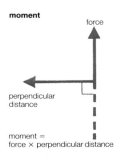

moment =
force × perpendicular distance

velocity ratio

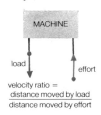

velocity ratio =
distance moved by load
distance moved by effort

mechanical advantage

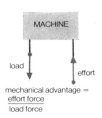

mechanical advantage =
effort force
load force

power (*n*) the rate at which work (p.17) is done,
or the rate at which energy is changed from one
form to another. Power = work done divided by
time taken.

watt (*n*) the SI unit (p.8) of power (↑). The power is
one watt if one joule (p.17) of work (p.17) is done
every second. **W** (*abbr*).

machine (*n*) a system for changing energy from
one form to another, or for allowing energy to be
used more easily.

lever (*n*) a simple machine (↑) which is made of
a stiff rod with a pivot (↓). A force (called the
effort (↓)) acts at one point on the lever and
tries to make it turn about the pivot. If a load is
placed on the lever closer to the pivot than the
effort, then the force on the load will be greater
than the effort, and the load can be moved more
easily than if no lever were used, though the
effort will have to move further than the load
moves.

effort (*n*) the force which does work (p.17) on a
machine (↑).

pivot (*n*) a fixed point about which a lever (↑) can
turn. Also known as **fulcrum**.

fulcrum (*n*) = pivot (↑).

moment (*n*) the force multiplied by the
perpendicular (p.234) distance from the point
about which the moment is being measured.
E.g. if a lever (↑) is in equilibrium (p.16), the
moments of the load and the effort (↑) about the
pivot (↑) will be equal, if there is no friction (p.15).
Also known as **torque**. SI unit (p.8): newton
(p.14) metre.

torque (*n*) = moment (↑).

velocity ratio for a machine (↑), the velocity ratio is
the distance moved by the effort (↑) divided by
the distance moved by the load. **V.R.** (*abbr*).

mechanical advantage for a machine (↑), the
mechanical advantage is the force (p.14)
produced on the load divided by the effort (↑). In
a perfect machine, i.e. one which is 100%
efficient (p.20), the mechanical advantage will be
equal to the velocity ratio (↑), but if there is
friction (p.15) the mechanical advantage will be
less than the velocity ratio. **M.A.** (*abbr*).

pulley system

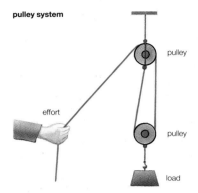

pulley

effort

pulley

load

pulley (*n*) a wheel around which a piece of string or
rope can run. In a pulley system, some pulleys
are fixed to a solid support, and some are fixed
to a block which has a hook on which a load can
be supported. The rope runs around the two
sets of pulleys. To lift the load by a given amount,
all the ropes supporting it must be shortened by
this amount. The amount of rope which must be
pulled out of the system by the effort (p.19)
is equal to the distance the load is to move
multiplied by the number of ropes which are
supporting it. The velocity ratio (p.19) of the
system will be equal to the number of ropes
supporting the load. The mechanical advantage
(p.19) will be less than the velocity ratio
because of the need to lift the lower pulleys and
their block as well as the load, and also because
of friction (p.15).

efficiency (*n*) the useful work (p.17) which is
done by a machine (p.19) divided by the
energy which is supplied to the machine.
efficient (*adj*).

percentage efficiency the efficiency (↑) of a
system multiplied by one hundred. A perfect
machine will have a percentage efficiency of
100%.

engine (*n*) a machine (p.19) for changing heat
energy (p.18) into some form of mechanical
energy (p.18).

momentum (*n*) = linear momentum (↓).
  momenta (*pl*).
linear momentum the mass of a body multiplied
  by its velocity (p.10). Momentum is a vector
  (p.10). SI unit (p.8): kilogram metre per second,
  or newton second (these are different names for
  the same unit).
law of conservation of momentum in any
  system in which no external forces (p.14) act, the
  linear momentum (↑) of the system (found by
  adding together all the momenta of the separate
  parts of the system) does not change.
impulse (*n*) a force (p.14) multiplied by the time for
  which it acts. The change in momentum (↑) of a
  body is equal to the impulse on it. SI unit (p.8):
  kilogram metre per second, or newton second
  (these are different names for the same unit).
elastic collision a collision (p.22) in which the
  kinetic energy (p.18) of the colliding bodies is the
  same after the collision as it was before, with no
  energy (p.17) being changed to other forms.

elastic collision   **inelastic collision**

kinetic energy before   kinetic energy after
collision = kinetic energy   collision < kinetic energy
after collision   before collision

inelastic collision a collision (p.22) in which the
  kinetic energy (p.18) after the collision is less
  than it was before, so some energy (p.17) has
  changed from kinetic energy to some other form,
  usually heat energy (p.18).
totally inelastic collision a collision (p.22) where
  the change in kinetic energy (p.18) is as large as
  possible. This happens when the two colliding
  bodies coalesce (↓).
coalesce (*v*) to come together to form a single
  object.

hyperelastic collision a collision (↓), or the event of two bodies being forced apart by an explosion, in which the kinetic energy (p.18) after is greater than it was before. This means that some other form of energy has been changed to kinetic energy, e.g. chemical energy (p.17) released by an explosion. When a gun is fired, the projectile (p.13) moves in one direction, while the gun *recoils*, i.e. moves backwards, with the same momentum as the projectile. This follows from the law of conservation of momentum (p.21).

collision (*n*) the act of two (or more) bodies hitting each other. **collide** (*v*).

hyperelastic collision

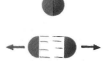

kinetic energy after collision > kinetic energy before collision

linear air track

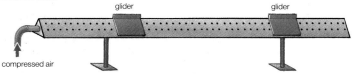

glider   glider

compressed air

linear air track an apparatus for the study of collisions (↑). Streams of air are blown through small holes in a straight track. These support metal vehicles called *gliders*, which can then move along the track with very little friction (p.15). Collisions between gliders can be arranged, and by changing the material at the end of the glider, elastic collisions (p.21), inelastic collisions (p.21) and hyperelastic collisions (↑) can be produced. The momenta (p.21) of the gliders can be found by measuring the mass of the gliders and their speed, which can be found by electronic (p.139) measurement.

CO_2 puck a metal ring with a flat metal plate on top. Solid carbon dioxide (dry ice) is trapped under the plate. As this turns to gas, the pressure (p.30) of the gas lifts the ring just above the surface on which it rests. The ring can then slide with very little friction (p.15). Pucks can be made to collide (↑) with each other, to show momentum (p.21) changes in collisions. Their velocity (p.10) is measured by stroboscopic photographs (p.11).

CO_2 puck

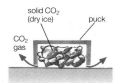

solid CO_2 (dry ice)   puck

CO_2 gas

gravity

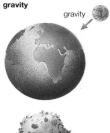

gravity

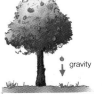

gravity

Newton's law of universal gravitation

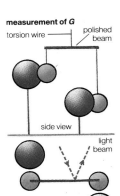

r

$$F = \frac{GmM}{r^2}$$

measurement of G

torsion wire

polished beam

side view

light beam

view from above

gravity (*n*) the effect of a mass in attracting (p.239) other masses towards itself. Usually noticed only when one of the masses is very large, e.g. a planet (p.26) or a star.

gravitation (*n*) the effect of one mass attracting (p.239) another towards itself. **gravitational** (*adj*).

Newton's law of universal gravitation if two masses *m* and *M* have a distance *r* between their centres of mass (p.24), then Newton's law states that the gravitational (↑) force between them will be GmM/r^2, where *G* is the universal gravitational constant (↓).

universal gravitational constant the fundamental constant (p.234) in Newton's law of universal gravitation (↑). $G = 6.7 \times 10^{-11}\ \mathrm{N\,m^2\,kg^{-2}}$, where *G* is the universal gravitational constant.

measurement of universal gravitational constant the universal gravitational constant (↑) is very small, with the result that it is difficult to measure. One way of measuring it uses the gravitational (↑) force between a pair of balls that are hung from a beam, and two larger balls, which can be moved closer or further away. The resulting moment (p.19) twists the fine thread on which the beam is hung. If the beam is polished and light reflected (p.45) off it, an optical lever (p.72) can be used to measure the twisting of the beam.

escape velocity the speed an object must have if it is to be able to escape from the gravitational field (↓) of a planet (p.26). At this speed, the kinetic energy (p.18) of the object is just equal to the gravitational potential energy (p.18) it has in the gravitational field. As the object moves away from the planet, the kinetic energy does work (p.17) against the gravitational force, and the object slows down.

escape velocity

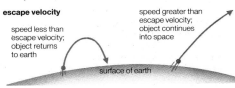

speed less than escape velocity; object returns to earth

speed greater than escape velocity; object continues into space

surface of earth

gravitational potential

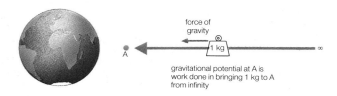

force of
gravity

A

∞

1 kg

gravitational potential at A is
work done in bringing 1 kg to A
from infinity

gravitational potential the work (p.17) that is
needed to bring a mass of one kilogram from
infinity to a particular point. Because the
gravitational (p.23) force is always attractive
(p.239), this means that work can always be
done by the gravitational field (↓) as an object is
brought towards the body that is attracting it, so
gravitational potential is always negative. The
gravitational potential energy (p.18) of a mass in
a gravitational field is equal to the mass multiplied
by the gravitational potential. SI unit (p.8): joule
(p.17) per kilogram.

weight (*n*) the force of gravity (p.23) at work on a
body.

centre of mass the point in a body where the
whole of the force of gravity (p.23) on that body
can be thought to act. In fact, in any body that is
not a single point, gravity acts on every point in
the body, but it is useful to think of gravity acting
at a single point, the centre of mass. The centre
of mass is the point about which the weights (↑)
of the particles that make up the body have no
total moment (p.19), whatever the direction of
gravity. The centre of mass of a body can be
found by hanging the body so that it can swing
freely; whatever point on the body is used as a
support, the centre of mass will always hang
directly below the support. Also known as
centre of gravity.

centre of gravity = centre of mass (↑).

gravitational field the gravitational (p.23) effect at
a point on a mass placed at that point. The
strength of the gravitational field is measured as
the force on each kilogram of the mass.

centre of mass

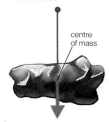

centre
of mass

object always hangs with
centre of mass directly below
support

acceleration in circular motion

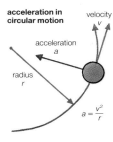

angular velocity

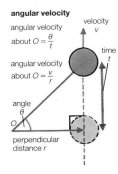

angular momentum

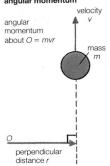

acceleration in circular motion when an object is moving in a circle at a constant (p.234) speed (p.10), it will be accelerating (p.12) towards the centre of the circle because its velocity (p.10) is always changing. The magnitude (p.10) of this acceleration is v^2/r, where v is the speed of the motion, and r is the radius of the circle.

angular velocity the rate of change (p.235) of the angle between an object and a fixed direction, seen from a particular point, e.g. for an object moving in a circle, the centre of that circle. For an object moving in a circle of radius r at a speed (p.10) v, the angular velocity about the centre of the circle is v/r. SI unit (p.8): radian (p.232) per second.

centripetal force the force that causes the acceleration (p.12) needed to make an object move in a circle. This is not a special type of force, but a simple force doing a particular thing, e.g. when a car goes around a bend, the centripetal force is provided by the friction (p.15) between the wheels and the road; if the road is wet, or the car tries to go around the corner too quickly, the limiting friction (p.15) may not be enough to cause the centripetal force needed, i.e. the car will not go around the corner. For an object of mass m moving in a circle of radius r at a speed v, the centripetal force will be mv^2/r.

centrifugal force an imaginary force, acting in the opposite direction to the centripetal force (↑). It is needed to make an object moving in a circle at constant (p.234) speed (p.10) appear to be in equilibrium (p.16). Such an object is not really in equilibrium, as its velocity (p.10) is changing.

angular momentum the linear momentum (p.21) of an object multiplied by its distance from a given point. For a body which is not a single point, but which is solid, it is found by adding together the angular momenta of all the points that make up the body. The rate of change (p.235) of the angular momentum of a body is equal to the couple (p.26) acting on the body. SI unit (p.8): kg m s^{-1}. **angular momenta** (*pl*).

moment of momentum = angular momentum (↑).

moment of inertia the angular momentum (p.25) of a solid body divided by its angular velocity (p.25). The moment of inertia is a measure of how easy it is to set the body turning about a given axis (↓). SI unit (p.8): kg m².

law of conservation of angular momentum for any system on which no couple (↓) acts, the angular momentum (p.25) of the system does not change.

axis (n) a line about which a body turns.

couple (n) a pair of forces, equal in size, but acting in opposite directions, with lines of action (p.239) which are not the same. The size of the couple is equal to the size of each of the forces multiplied by the perpendicular (p.234) distance between them. A couple will cause a body to try to turn, without moving its centre of mass (p.24). A single force producing a moment (p.19) can be thought of as a couple together with a force acting on the centre of mass.

orbit (n) the path that a planet (↓) or satellite (↓) takes around some larger body, with the centripetal force (p.25) being the force of gravity (p.23) between them. The path that is taken may be a hyperbola (p.234), in which case the orbit is open, or it may be an ellipse (p.234), of which a special case is the circular orbit. Planets move in orbits which are very nearly circles. **orbit** (v).

satellite (n) an object which is in orbit (↑) around a larger body.

planet (n) a large mass of rock or rock and gas that is in orbit (↑) around a star, particularly the sun.

Kepler's first law planets (↑) move in orbits (↑) which are ellipses (p.234), with the sun at one focus (p.71).

Kepler's second law the area swept out in a given time by a line joining a planet (↑) to the sun is always the same, wherever in the orbit (↑) this quantity is measured.

Kepler's third law the square of the time taken for a planet (↑) to complete one orbit (↑) is proportional (p.235) to the third power of the average radius of the orbit.

couple

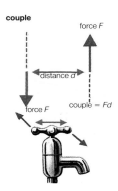

force F

distance d

force F

couple = Fd

orbit

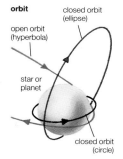

closed orbit (ellipse)

open orbit (hyperbola)

star or planet

closed orbit (circle)

Kepler's second law

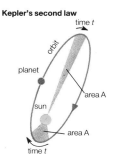

time t

orbit

planet

area A

sun

area A

time t

circumpolar orbit

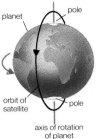

motion of planet means every point on the surface will pass under the orbit of the satellite

circumpolar orbit an orbit (↑) which passes through the axis (↑) of the body that is being orbited. In the case of an orbit around the Earth, a circumpolar orbit will pass over the north and south poles. As the Earth is turning about its axis, in time the orbit will pass over every part of the Earth.

geostationary orbit an orbit (↑) around the Earth, which has such a direction and distance from the Earth that the body orbits at the same rate as the Earth turns. Seen from the Earth, a body in geostationary orbit always seems to be in the same place in the sky.

geostationary orbit

time for satellite to complete one orbit: 24 hours

weightlessness (*n*) when a satellite (↑) is in orbit (↑), objects free to move inside it float around as if they have no weight (p.24). The force of gravity (p.23) still acts on these objects but because both they and the satellite that contains them are falling freely, they all have the same acceleration (p.12), and so no contact force (p.14) is needed to hold them in place.

centrifuge (*n*) a machine that is used for separating small solid particles from a liquid in which they are moving. It works by turning the material very rapidly. The centripetal force (p.25) that is needed causes the denser (p.28) material to move in larger circles than the less dense material.

centrifuge

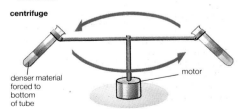

denser material forced to bottom of tube

motor

density

same volumes, different masses

$$\text{density} = \frac{\text{mass}}{\text{volume}}$$

same masses, different volumes:

   |

| 1 m³ lead mass 11 400 kg | 1 m³ water mass 1000 kg | 1 m³ air mass 1.3 kg | 1 kg aluminium 370 cm³ | 1 kg copper 110 cm³ | 1 kg gold 52 cm³ |

density (*n*) the mass of a body divided by its
volume (p.55). The density will be the same for
any object made of a given material and is a
measure of how the mass of a body of a given
size depends on the material from which it is
made. SI unit (p.8): kg m^{-3}, though the non SI
unit of gram per centimetre cubed (g cm^{-3}) is
also often used.

dense (*adj*) having a large density (↑).

displacement can a container with an overflow,
which can be used to measure the volume (p.55)
of solid bodies which do not have a shape whose
volume can easily be measured. The
displacement can is filled to the overflow with
liquid and the body whose volume is to be
measured is lowered into the liquid. The volume
of liquid coming out of the overflow is equal to
the volume displaced (↓) by the body, which will
be equal to the volume of the body as long as it
sinks. If the body floats, it must be pulled below
the liquid surface with a denser (↑) object. Also
known as **eureka can**.

eureka can = displacement can (↑).

sinker (*n*) a weight used to pull an object below the
surface of the liquid used in a displacement can
(↑) so its density (↑) can be measured.

hydrometer (*n*) an instrument for measuring the
density (↑) of liquids. It is a glass tube with a
weight at the bottom, so it floats upright. The
height at which it floats in a liquid depends on the
density of that liquid (*see principle of flotation* (↓))
and this can be read from a scale on the
hydrometer.

relative density the density (↑) of a material
divided by the density of water. Also known as
specific gravity.

specific gravity = relative density (↑).

displacement can

volume of
object = *V*

displacement
can

volume of
water = *V*

hydrometer

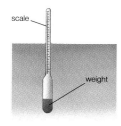

scale

weight

Archimedes' principle

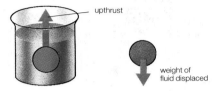

upthrust

weight of
fluid displaced

upthrust = weight of fluid displaced

Archimedes' principle when a body is placed in a
fluid (p.30), there is a force upwards on it that is
equal to the weight (p.24) of the fluid displaced
(↓).

upthrust (*n*) the upward force on an object which
is placed in a fluid (p.30).

displacement (*n*) the volume (p.55) of fluid (p.30)
pushed out of the way when a solid body is
placed in the fluid. **displace** (*v*).

buoyancy (*n*) the measure of the amount by which
a body tends to float. **buoyant** (*adj*).

principle of flotation a body will float when the
weight (p.24) of the fluid (p.30) it displaces (↑) is
equal to its own weight. The less dense (↑) the
body, the higher it will float. Bodies which have a
density greater than the fluid in which they are
placed will not float at all. This is a result of
Archimedes' principle (↑).

principle of flotation

an object floats when its weight equals
the weight of fluid displaced

weight of water
displaced

weight
of ship

pressure (*n*) a force divided by the area over which that force acts. Pressure may be caused by the weight (p.24) of material pressing on a surface, or by the collisions (p.22) of the atoms (p.139) or molecules (p.188) of a gas with the walls of the container that is holding it. Pressure acts equally in all directions, which means that although a pressure may be due to the force of gravity (p.23) on a fluid (↓), the pressure up will be the same as the pressure down.

pascal (*n*) the SI unit (p.8) of pressure (↑). A pressure of one pascal is a force of one newton (p.14) on each square metre of area. **Pa** (*abbr*).

hydrostatic pressure pressure (↑) that is caused by the force of gravity (p.23) on a fluid (↓) which is not moving. If the density (p.28) of the fluid is *ρ*, and the strength of gravity (p.23) is *g*, the pressure at a distance *h* below the surface of the liquid will be greater than any surface pressure, e.g. atmospheric pressure (↓), by *ρgh*.

pressure

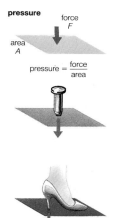

$$pressure = \frac{force}{area}$$

pointed objects produce higher pressures for the same force

hydrostatic pressure

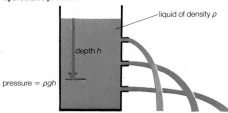

liquid of density *ρ*

depth *h*

pressure = *ρgh*

fluid (*n*) a liquid or a gas.

manometer (*n*) an instrument that is used for measuring pressure (↑). It is made of a U-shaped tube containing a liquid of known density (p.28). The difference in levels of the liquid on each side of the tube is a measure of the different pressures on the two sides of the tube. If one side of the tube is closed and contains a vacuum (p.242) above the liquid, then the absolute pressure (↓) on the other side of the tube can be measured, rather than the pressure difference between the two sides of the tube.

manometer

open to air at pressure P_2

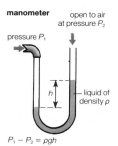

pressure P_1

h

liquid of density *ρ*

$P_1 - P_2 = \rho gh$

barometer

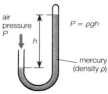

air
pressure
P

h

$P = \rho g h$

mercury
(density ρ)

**Torricelli
vacuum**

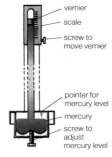

Torricelli
vacuum

Fortin barometer

vernier

scale

screw to
move vernier

pointer for
mercury level

mercury

screw to
adjust
mercury level

aneroid barometer

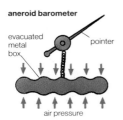

evacuated
metal
box

pointer

air pressure

absolute pressure pressure (↑) measured from
zero pressure rather than pressure measured
from some existing pressure, e.g. atmospheric
pressure (↓).

atmosphere (*n*) the gases held around a planet
(p.26), particularly the Earth, by its gravity (p.23).
atmospheric (*adj*).

atmospheric pressure the hydrostatic pressure
(↑) in an atmosphere (↑). On the Earth at sea
level, atmospheric pressure is about 1.01×10^5
Pa, but it varies with changing weather
conditions.

barometer (*n*) an instrument that is used for
measuring atmospheric pressure (↑). A simple
barometer is made from a J-shaped glass tube,
open at the short end, and filled with mercury.
The difference in the height of mercury between
the two sides is a measure of the atmospheric
pressure.

torr (*n*) a non SI unit (p.8) of pressure (↑). One torr
is the pressure produced by a one millimetre
depth of mercury in the Earth's gravity (p.23).

bar (*n*) a non SI unit (p.8) of pressure. One bar is
equal to 10^5 pascal (p.30).

Torricelli vacuum the vacuum (p.242) above the
liquid in the closed side of a barometer (↑). It is
not a perfect vacuum, but contains vapour
(p.195) from the liquid in the barometer at its
saturated vapour pressure (p.195).

Fortin barometer a type of barometer (↑) which
measures atmospheric pressure (↑) by finding
the height of mercury that the atmospheric
pressure can support. It is fitted with a vernier
scale (p.239) for accurate (p.240) readings.

aneroid barometer a barometer (↑) which
contains a metal box in which there is no air and
into which no air can enter. The shape of this box
changes slightly as the atmospheric pressure (↑)
changes, and these changes are shown by a
pointer and scale.

Bourdon gauge an instrument for measuring the
pressure (↑) in a fluid (↑). The fluid is fed into a
curved metal tube which becomes straighter as
the pressure inside it increases. This change is
shown by a pointer and scale.

viscosity (*n*) a measure of how difficult it is to force a solid object of a given shape through a fluid (p.30) at a given speed (p.10), or of how difficult it is to force a fluid past a solid body, e.g. down a pipe. Viscosity depends only on the fluid and not on the shape or size of the solid body or on how fast the fluid is moving. **viscous** (*adj*).

air resistance the force which tends to slow down any object moving through the air. It increases with the relative velocity (p.11) of the object through the air. For simple purposes, air resistance is taken as being proportional (p.235) to the speed (p.10) of the air flow, but in fact the behaviour of the force is much less simple, particularly at high speed. In turbulent (↓) flow, the force is more nearly proportional to the velocity squared.

terminal velocity the velocity (p.10) of an object falling under gravity (p.23), at which the force of air resistance (↑) is as great as the weight (p.24) of the object. Once the object has reached this velocity, it will not accelerate (p.12) any further.

Stokes' law for a round ball of radius *a*, moving at a speed (p.10) *v*, through a fluid (p.30) of viscosity (↑) *η*, the viscous force on the ball will be $6\pi\eta a v$, as long as the ball is moving slowly enough for the flow to be laminar (↓) rather than turbulent (↓).

turbulent (*adj*) of the flow of a fluid (p.30) which is not smooth, but which instead has an uneven motion.

laminar (*adj*) of the smooth flow of a fluid (p.30), with each part of the fluid moving at nearly the same velocity (p.10) as the next part.

air resistance

coin falls faster than feather because it produces less air resistance for its weight

terminal velocity

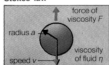

terminal velocity low | terminal velocity high

air resistance = weight

Stokes' law

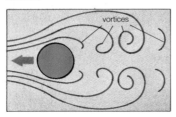

force of viscosity *F*

radius *a*

viscosity of fluid *η*

speed *v*

$F = 6\pi\eta a v$

turbulent

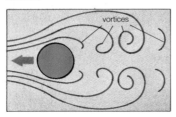

vortices

laminar

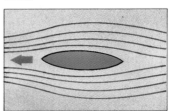

boundary layer the fluid (p.30) close to the surface of a solid body, which moves with that solid body when it moves through the rest of the fluid.

Bernoulli effect

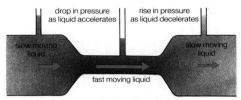

same volume of fluid per second flows through all parts of the tube

Bernoulli effect the change in pressure produced when a fluid (p.30) is accelerated when it is forced into a narrow space; it must accelerate (p.12) if the rate of flow is to remain the same (as it must). According to Newton's second law (p.14), this acceleration means there must be a force; this comes from the difference in pressure (p.30) caused by the fluid accelerating. The pressure is lower in the area where the fluid is moving faster.

aerofoil

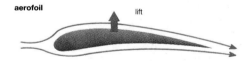

aerofoil (*n*) a shape which is more strongly curved on the top surface than the bottom, so when the aerofoil moves through the air, air must move faster over the top than over the bottom. According to the Bernoulli effect (↑) this causes an up force. This is the way that aeroplane wings work.

lift (*n*) the up force which is produced by an aerofoil (↑).

drag (*n*) the viscous (↑) force which tends to slow down objects moving through a fluid (p.30).

special theory of relativity a theory (p.238) which states that there is no special point of view from which science should be studied. The laws of physics (p.238) will be the same for any person in any inertial frame of reference (↓). An important starting point of the theory is that the speed of light (p.59) is constant (p.234).

general theory of relativity a theory (p.238) which allows the ideas of the special theory of relativity (↑) to be used for non-inertial frames of reference (↓). In this theory, gravity (p.23) and acceleration (p.12) are very closely related.

constancy of speed of light

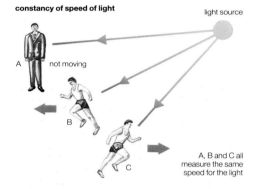

light source

A   not moving

B

C

A, B and C all measure the same speed for the light

constancy of speed of light according to the special theory of relativity (↑) the speed of light (p.59) will be the same even if the person measuring this speed is moving towards or away from the object that produces the light. Thus there is no special point of view from which the speed of light should be measured.

inertial frame of reference a point of view from which Newton's first law (p.14) of motion seems to be true. An inertial frame of reference does not appear to be accelerating (p.12) when seen from any other inertial frame of reference.

relativistic (*adj*) moving at a speed close enough to the speed of light (p.59) for the differences between the special theory of relativity (↑) and Newton's laws (p.14) to be important.

simple harmonic motion

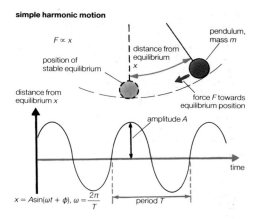

$x = A\sin(\omega t + \phi)$, $\omega = \dfrac{2\pi}{T}$

simple harmonic motion motion in which a body
moves so that its distance from its equilibrium
(p.16) position varies sinusoidally (p.234) with
time. A system will show simple harmonic motion
when it is moved from a position of stable
equilibrium (p.16), if the force trying to return the
body to its equilibrium position is proportional
(p.235) to the distance from that position. This
will be true for any position of stable equilibrium
as long as the oscillations ($\downarrow$) are small enough.
Simple harmonic motion can be described by
the equation $x = A\sin(\omega t + \phi)$, where x is the
distance from the equilibrium position, A is the
amplitude (p.36) of the motion, ω is its angular
frequency (p.37), t is the time, and ϕ is the phase
(p.37) relative to an oscillation which is at its
equilibrium position and moving so that x is
increasing, at time $t = 0$. **s.h.m.** (*abbr*).

oscillation (*n*) the motion of a body or system
which moves in such a way that the motion
repeats after a fixed time. One oscillation is the
motion from the equilibrium (p.16) position to the
point where the body or system is again in its
equilibrium position and moving in the same
direction, or any other part of the motion which
takes the same time. **oscillate** (*v*).

amplitude (*n*) the largest distance of an oscillating (p.35) system from its equilibrium (p.16) position.

period (*n*) the time that is taken for one oscillation (p.35); the shortest time between two moments when an oscillating body is in the same position, and is moving in the same direction. Period is the reciprocal (p.235) of frequency (↓).

frequency (*n*) the number of oscillations (p.35) completed in one second. Frequency is the reciprocal (p.235) of period (↑). SI unit (p.8): hertz (↓).

hertz (*n*) the SI unit (p.8) of frequency (↑). The frequency of a system is one hertz if the system completes one oscillation (p.35) each second. **Hz** (*abbr*).

simple pendulum a mass on the end of a length of string or other freely-moving support. If the mass is moved from its equilibrium (p.16) position (directly below the support) and released, it will oscillate (p.35) about that position. If the distance from equilibrium is not too great, and air resistance (p.32) is small, the motion will be simple harmonic motion (p.35), with a period $2\pi \, (l/g)^{1/2}$, where *l* is the distance of the centre of mass (p.24) of the pendulum from the support, and *g* is the strength of gravity (p.12).

bob (*n*) the mass on the end of a simple pendulum (↑).

spring pendulum a mass fixed to one end of a spring, the other end of which is fixed. If the mass is moved from its equilibrium (p.16) position and released, it will oscillate (p.35). If the spring obeys Hooke's law (p.224), and air resistance (p.32) is not too large, the motion will be simple harmonic motion (p.35), with a period (↑) $2\pi \, (m/k)^{1/2}$, where *m* is the mass on the end of the spring (assumed to be much greater than the mass of the spring itself), and *k* is the spring constant (p.224) of the spring.

conical pendulum a simple pendulum (↑) which has been set moving in such a way that the bob (↑) does not move in a plane (p.233), but in a circle.

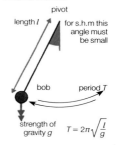

simple pendulum

pivot

length *l*

for s.h.m this angle must be small

bob

period *T*

strength of gravity *g*

$$T = 2\pi\sqrt{\dfrac{l}{g}}$$

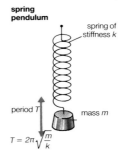

spring pendulum

spring of stiffness *k*

period *T*

mass *m*

$$T = 2\pi\sqrt{\dfrac{m}{k}}$$

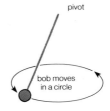

conical pendulum

pivot

bob moves in a circle

phase

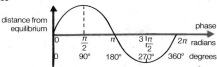

phase[1] (*n*) the measure of the amount by which two oscillating (p.35) systems with similar frequencies (↑) are at different stages of their oscillation at a given time. Phase is measured as an angle, each oscillation being 360°, or 2π radians (p.232).

in phase of two oscillating (p.35) systems which are at the same stage of their oscillations at a given time.

in phase, out of phase

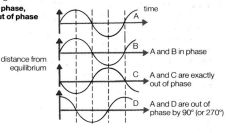

out of phase (1) of two oscillating (p.35) systems which are not at the same stage of their oscillations at a given time; (2) exactly out of phase (↓).

exactly out of phase of two oscillating (p.35) systems which are at exactly opposite stages of their oscillations at a given time, so that the phase difference (↓) between them is 180°.

phase difference the difference in phase (↑) between two oscillations (p.35).

angular frequency 2π times frequency (↑). For simple harmonic motion (p.35) the acceleration (p.12) is $-\omega^2 x$, where x is the distance from the equilibrium (p.16) position, and ω is the angular frequency. The minus sign shows that the acceleration is *towards* the equilibrium position.

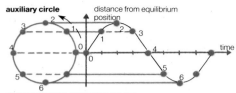

object moving in a circle at fixed speed

auxiliary circle a way of finding the equations for simple harmonic motion (p.35). If a body moves around a circle with a constant (p.234) speed (p.10), the projection (p.233) of the motion onto a line will be a point which moves with simple harmonic motion.

energy in simple harmonic motion in simple harmonic motion (p.35), energy changes between potential energy (p.17) and kinetic energy (p.18), but the amount of kinetic energy plus potential energy always remains the same (*see law of conservation of energy* (p.18)). The kinetic energy is largest and the potential energy smallest in the middle of the motion, at the equilibrium (p.16) position. The potential energy is largest and the kinetic energy is zero at each end of the motion, when the body is furthest from the equilibrium position.

energy in simple harmonic motion

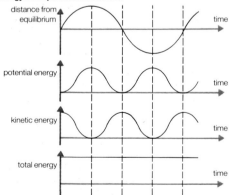

damped harmonic motion

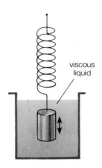

viscous
liquid

damped oscillations oscillations (p.35) in which
friction (p.15) or viscosity (p.32) are important. In
damped oscillations the amplitude (p.36) is not
fixed, but gets less with time. **damping** (*n*).
damp (*v*).

damping force the force which causes the
amplitude (p.36) of a damped oscillation (↑) to
get smaller. It is a force which always acts in the
opposite direction to the motion of the oscillating
body.

decay constant the reciprocal (p.235) of time
taken for the amplitude (p.36) of an oscillation
(p.35) to fall to $1/e$ times its starting value, where
$e = 2.713$. If the damping force (↑) is proportional (p.235) to the speed (p.10) of the oscillating
body, with a constant of proportionality (p.235)
k, the decay constant will be $k/(2m)$, where *m* is
the mass of the oscillating body.

distance from equilibrium   **decay constant**   distance from equilibrium

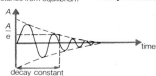

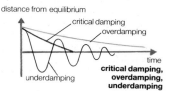

critical damping
overdamping

time

**critical damping,
overdamping,
underdamping**

underdamping

critical damping the amount of damping (↑) that
causes an oscillating (p.35) system to come to
rest as quickly as possible, and without going
past the equilibrium (p.16) position. For critical
damping, the decay constant (↑) must be equal
to the angular frequency (p.37) of the
oscillations.

underdamping (*n*) damping (↑) which is less than
critical damping (↑). Thus the system, once
moved away from its equilibrium (p.16) position
and released, will pass through the equilibrium
position and complete several oscillations (p.35)
before stopping.

overdamping (*n*) damping (↑) which is more than
critical damping (↑), so the oscillating (p.35)
system, moved away from its equilibrium (p.16)
position and released, will return slowly, without
going past the equilibrium position.

forced oscillation the motion of an oscillating
(p.35) system which is acted on not only by the
forces trying to return the system to its
equilibrium (p.16) position, but also by a force
which itself oscillates at a frequency (p.36) which
may be different from the natural frequency (↓) of
the oscillating system. The oscillating system will
settle to the same frequency as the driving force
(↓), but the amplitude (p.36) and the phase
difference (p.37) between the oscillations and the
driving force depend on how the driving
frequency compares with the natural frequency.

driving force a force producing forced oscillations
(↑).

natural frequency the frequency (p.36) at which a
system will oscillate (p.35) if there is no driving
force (↑).

resonance (*n*) the state in which the natural
frequency (↑) of an oscillating (p.35) system is
the same as the frequency (p.36) of the driving
force (↑). At resonance the amplitude (p.36) will
be largest and the phase (p.37) of the oscillating
system will be 90° behind the driving force. The
amplitude of the oscillations at resonance will be
less if the system is strongly damped (p.39), and
with strong damping the change in amplitude as
the driving frequency moves away from the
natural frequency is less rapid.

forced oscillation

driving
force

forced oscillation

resonance

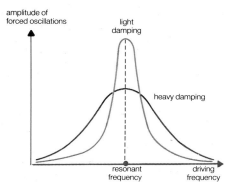

amplitude of
forced oscillations

light
damping

heavy damping

resonant   driving
frequency   frequency

phase relationships in forced oscillations

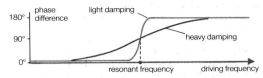

phase relationships in forced oscillations if the driving frequency (p.36) is much less than the natural frequency (↑), the motion of the oscillating (p.35) system will be in phase (p.37) with the driving force (↑). If the frequency of the driving force is much higher than the natural frequency, the motion of the oscillating system will be exactly out of phase (p.37) with the driving force. At resonance (↑) the phase difference (p.37) is 90°, with the motion of the oscillating system being behind the driving force. The sharpness of the change of phase as the frequency of the driving force passes through the natural frequency depends on the amount of damping (p.39). The phase change is sharpest for lightly damped systems.

Q-factor (n) a measure of the amount of damping (p.39) in an oscillating (p.35) system. The Q-factor is 2π times the energy stored in the oscillating system divided by the energy lost in a single oscillation.

Barton's pendulums an example of the behaviour of forced oscillations (↑). A single heavy pendulum (p.239) is fixed to a flexible (p.226) support to which several lighter pendulums of various lengths are also fixed. When the heavy pendulum is set in motion, the other pendulums begin to move. The light pendulum which has the same length as the heavy pendulum has the largest amplitude (p.36), and the phase differences (p.37) can also be seen.

Barton's pendulums

wave

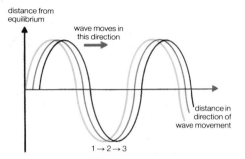

distance from equilibrium

wave moves in this direction

distance in direction of wave movement

$1 \rightarrow 2 \rightarrow 3$

wave (*n*) a motion which is carried through long distances in a material with no single part of the material ever moving far from its equilibrium (p. 16) position. The motion of one part of the system causes a motion of the nearby parts. Also known as **travelling wave** or **progressive wave** to avoid confusion with standing wave (p. 52).

travelling wave = wave (↑).
progressive wave = wave (↑).

transverse wave

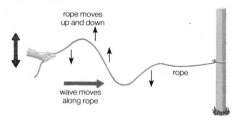

rope moves up and down

rope

wave moves along rope

transverse wave a wave (↑) in which the motion of the single particles from their equilibrium (p. 16) positions is at 90° to the direction in which the wave is travelling. Surface waves in water and waves on a long piece of string are examples of transverse waves.

longitudinal wave

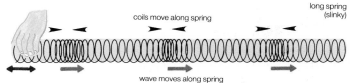

coils move along spring

long spring
(slinky)

wave moves along spring

longitudinal wave a wave (↑) in which the motion
of the single particles from their equilibrium (p. 16)
positions is in the same direction as the direction
in which the wave is travelling. Sound waves and
waves on a long spring are examples of
longitudinal waves.

polarized

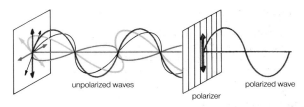

unpolarized waves

polarized wave

polarizer

polarized (*adj*) of a transverse wave (↑) where
there is a particular direction of motion for the
particles in the wave.
unpolarized (*adj*) of a transverse wave (↑) in which
the particles may move in any direction which is
at 90° to the direction of the wave motion.
wavelength (*n*) the closest distance between two
points in a wave (↑) which are moving in phase
(p. 37). Wavelength is inversely proportional
(p. 235) to frequency (p. 36).

wavelength

distance from
equilibrium position

distance in
direction of
wave
motion

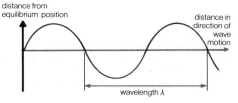

wavelength λ

wavenumber (*n*) the reciprocal (p.235) of the wave-length (p.43) or 2π divided by the wavelength. Confusingly, both these quantities are referred to as wavenumber. The wavenumber of a wave is proportional (p.235) to its frequency (p.36).

power carried by a wave the power (p.19) carried by a wave (p.42) is proportional (p.235) to the speed (p.10) of the wave, and is also proportional to the square of its amplitude (p.36), and to the square of its frequency (p.36).

intensity (*n*) the intensity of a wave (p.42) is equal to the power (p.19) carried by the wave divided by the area over which that power arrives. SI unit (p.8): W m^{-2}. **intense** (*adj*).

wavefront (*n*) a line that joins all the points on a wave (p.42) which have the same phase (p.37). E.g. a wavefront in a plane (p.233) polarized (p.43) transverse wave (p.42), such as a wave on a water surface, may be a set of lines which show the positions of all the points on the wave which are furthest above the equilibrium (p.16) position. These points are called the *crests* of the wave.

wavefront

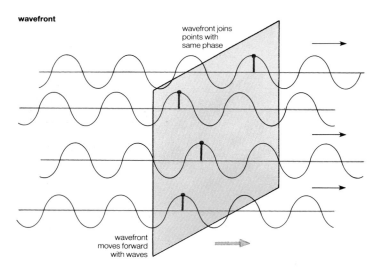

wavefront joins points with same phase

wavefront moves forward with waves

reflection

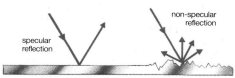

non-specular
reflection

specular
reflection

reflection, reflexion (*n*) the act of a wave (p.42)
striking the border between the material in which
the wave is travelling, and some other material,
which may or may not be able to support the
wave, with the wave remaining in the first
material but now travelling in a different direction.
reflect (*v*). **reflective** (*adj*).

specular (*adj*) of the type of reflection (↑) that
happens at a border between two materials
when the border is smooth, i.e. the size of any
unevenness is much less than the wavelength
(p.43) of the wave (p.42) being reflected. In
specular reflection, the reflected wave moves in
a direction which depends only on the angle of
incidence (↓) of the incident (↓) wave. Also
known as **regular**.

specular reflection

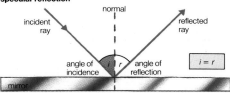

normal

incident
ray

reflected
ray

angle of
incidence

angle of
reflection

$$i = r$$

mirror

regular (*adj*) = specular (↑).

incident (*adj*) incoming, particularly when used of
a wave (p.42) or ray (p.59) of light.

angle of incidence the angle between the
direction of motion of an incident (↑) wave (p.42)
and the normal (p.234) at the border between
two materials.

angle of reflection the angle between the
direction of motion of a reflected (↑) wave (p.42)
and the normal (p.234) at the border between
two materials.

laws of reflection for regular (p.45) reflection
(p.45), the angle of incidence (p.45) is equal to
the angle of reflection (p.45), and the directions
of the incident (p.45) and reflected (p.45) waves
(p.42) and the normal (p.234) lie in the same
plane (p.233).

refraction (*n*) the change in direction of a wave
(p.42) when it passes from one material into
another. These effects are caused by the speed
(p.10) of the wave being different in the two
materials. The frequency (p.36) of the wave will
not change as it moves from one material to
another, but the wavelength (p.43) will be less in
the material in which the wave travels more
slowly. If the wave does not hit the border
between the two materials at 90°, the direction of
the wave will also change on crossing the
border. The wave will travel closer to the normal
(p.234) direction in the material in which it travels
most slowly. **refract** (*v*).

refraction

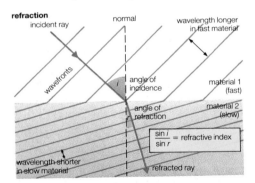

incident ray · normal · wavelength longer in fast material · wavefronts · angle of incidence · *i* · material 1 (fast) · angle of refraction · material 2 (slow) · $\dfrac{\sin i}{\sin r}$ = refractive index · wavelength shorter in slow material · refracted ray

angle of refraction the angle between the
direction in which a wave (p.42) travels after it
has crossed the border between two materials
and the normal (p.234) to that border.

Snell's law in refraction (↑) the sine of the angle of
incidence (p.45) of a wave (p.42) divided by the
sine of the angle of refraction of the wave is a
constant (p.234). This constant is called the
refractive index (↓).

refractive index the constant (p.234) in Snell's
law (↑). It is also equal to the speed (p.10) of the
wave (p.42) in the first material divided by the
speed of the wave in the second material. If a
refractive index is given for a single material, the
first material is taken to be a vacuum (p.242).

phase change on reflection when a wave (p.42) is
reflected (p.45) at the border between two
materials, the phase (p.37) of the reflected wave
depends on the speed (p.10) of the wave in the
two materials. If the speed in the reflecting material would have been less, there is a 180° phase
change between the incident (p.45) and reflected
waves. If the speed in the reflecting material
would have been more, there is no phase change.

total internal reflection

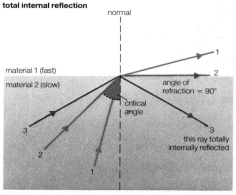

total internal reflection the reflection (p.45) of a
wave (p.42) passing from a material in which it
moves more slowly to a material in which it
moves more quickly where refraction (↑) would
result in an angle of refraction (↑) greater than
90° so there can be no refraction. All the light is
then reflected and none refracted.

critical angle the smallest angle of incidence
(p.45) at which a given material can produce
total internal reflection (↑). This angle of
incidence is the one which would produce an
angle of refraction (↑) of 90°.

interference

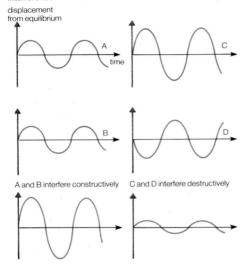

displacement
from equilibrium

A and B interfere constructively   C and D interfere destructively

interference (*n*) the effect of two or more waves
(p.42) arriving at the same point by different
paths or from different places. If the principle of
superposition (p.50) is true, the resulting effect
can be found by adding together the effects that
each wave would have had if they had been
present separately. **interfere** (*v*).

constructive (*adj*) of interference (↑) in which two
waves (p.42) of similar frequencies (p.36) arrive
in phase (p.37). Thus the resulting wave motion
has an amplitude (p.36) which is found by adding
together the amplitudes of each of the waves. If
two waves of equal amplitude interfere
constructively, the resulting motion will have an
amplitude twice as great as either of the waves
on its own, and four times the energy. Two
waves which start in phase with one another will
interfere constructively if they arrive after having
travelled along paths which are the same length
or which are different in length by a whole
number of wavelengths (p.43).

destructive (*adj*) of interference (↑) in which two
waves (p.42) of similar frequencies (p.36) arrive
exactly out of phase (p.37). Thus the resulting
motion has an amplitude (p.36) equal to the
difference between the amplitudes of the two
waves. If the two waves have the same
amplitude they will destroy each other
completely. Two waves which start in phase with
one another will cause destructive interference if
they arrive after having travelled along paths
which are different in length by a whole number
(including zero) of wavelengths (p.43) and one
half of a wavelength.

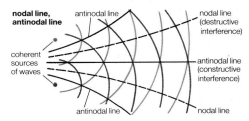

nodal line a line joining points where there is
destructive (↑) interference (↑).
antinodal line a line joining points where there is
constructive (↑) interference (↑).
coherent (*adj*) of waves (p.42), or things making
waves, where there is a fixed phase difference
(p.37) between one part of the wave and
another, or between waves from one place and
another. E.g. two light waves which have come
from the same light by way of different paths will
be coherent, unlike two light waves which have
come from different lights, the phases of the
motions of the atoms (p.139) in the two lights
being unrelated and always changing.

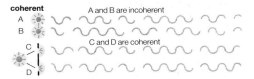

beats

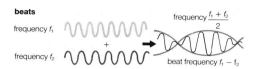

frequency f_1

frequency f_2

$+$

frequency $\dfrac{f_1 + f_2}{2}$

beat frequency $f_1 - f_2$

beat (*n*) the effect of two waves (p.42) of slightly
different frequencies (p.36) coming together and
interfering (p.48). The interference at any point
will change from being constructive (p.48) to
destructive (p.49) and back again as the waves
move in and out of phase (p.37) with one
another. The result is that the amplitude (p.36) of
the resulting motion will change between being
larger than the amplitudes of the two separate
waves and being equal to the difference between
their amplitudes. The frequency of this change in
amplitude will be equal to the difference between
the frequencies of the waves. This variation
modulates (↓) the amplitude of a wave which will
have a frequency equal to the average frequency
of the two waves. **beat** (*v*).

beat frequency the frequency (p.36) at which the
amplitude (p.36) of two beating (↑) waves (p.42)
varies, i.e. the difference between the
frequencies of the two separate waves.

modulate (*v*) to change the amplitude (p.36),
phase (p.37) or frequency (p.36) of a wave
(p.42), usually over a time much longer than the
period (p.36) of the wave. **modulation** (*n*).

principle of superposition the idea that the effect
caused by more than one wave (p.42) can be
found simply by adding together the effect that
each wave would produce on its own.

diffraction (*n*) the spreading out of a wave (p.42)
after it has gone around a solid object or after it
has passed through a space between solid
objects. If the size of the space is only a few
times the wavelength (p.43) of the wave, then the
wave will spread out noticeably after passing
through it. If the size of the space is about equal
to, or less than, the wavelength, the diffraction
will be so great that the wave can be thought of
as spreading out in all directions on the far side
of the space. **diffract** (*v*).

diffraction

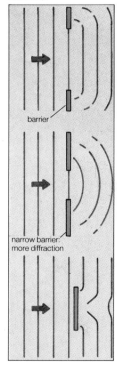

barrier

narrow barrier:
more diffraction

Huygens' construction

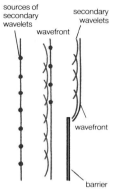

sources of secondary wavelets

secondary wavelets

wavefront

wavefront

barrier

diffraction pattern the changes in intensity (p.44) of a wave (p.42) caused by diffraction (↑).

Huygens' construction a way of finding how a wave (p.42) will behave after it has been diffracted (↑), refracted (p.46) or reflected (p.45). Each point on the wavefront (p.44) is thought of as a source of circular waves, called secondary wavelets, which spread out from that point. The position of the next wavefront forward can be found by joining the leading edges of these circular waves.

secondary wavelet *see* Huygens' construction (↑).

diffraction at a single slit a wave (p.42) of wavelength (p.43) λ passing through a single slit of width a, where the height of the slit is much greater than λ, will spread out on the far side of the slit, with greatest intensity (p.44) in the forward direction. There will be zero intensity at angles θ to the forward direction, where $\sin\theta = n\lambda/a$, where n is a whole number. The areas where there is zero intensity are caused by destructive (p.49) interference (p.48) of waves coming from different parts of the slit.

diffraction at a single slit

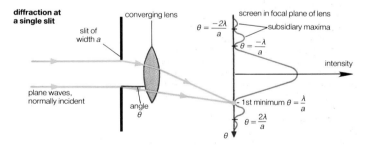

converging lens

slit of width a

plane waves, normally incident

angle θ

screen in focal plane of lens

$\theta = \dfrac{-2\lambda}{a}$

subsidiary maxima

$\theta = \dfrac{-\lambda}{a}$

intensity

1st minimum $\theta = \dfrac{\lambda}{a}$

$\theta = \dfrac{2\lambda}{a}$

θ

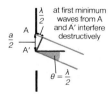

at first minimum waves from A and A' interfere destructively

$\dfrac{\lambda}{2}$

A

$\dfrac{a}{2}$

A'

$\theta = \dfrac{\lambda}{2}$

subsidiary maximum a maximum (p.235) of intensity (p.44) in a diffraction pattern (↑) which is not in the forward direction. They appear in directions where there is constructive (p.48) interference (p.48) between waves (p.42) which have passed through different parts of an opening. Subsidiary maxima become less intense as their angle from the forward direction increases.

standing wave the motion set up in a material in which there are two progressive waves (p.42) of equal frequency (p.36) and similar amplitudes (p.36), travelling in opposite directions. At some points in the material the waves will be in phase (p.37), so constructive (p.48) interference (p.48) will cause the oscillation (p.35) of the material at this point to be at its largest. At other points, the waves will be exactly out of phase (p.37), so destructive (p.49) interference will cause the amplitude of the oscillations of the material at these points to be small, or zero if the two waves have the same amplitude. A standing wave can be set up by making a wave and arranging for it to be reflected (p.45) at the borders of the material in which it travels. If, after the wave has been reflected at both ends of the material, it is in phase with the original wave, a standing wave will be set up. Also known as **stationary wave**.

stationary wave = standing wave (↑).

node (*n*) a point on a standing wave (↑) where the oscillation (p.35) is at its smallest.

antinode (*n*) a point on a standing wave (↑) where the oscillation (p.35) is at its largest.

standing waves on a string standing waves (↑) can be set up on a stretched string at those frequencies (p.36) where twice the length of the string is equal to a whole number of wavelengths (p.43). There will be nodes (↑) at each end of the string, and if the string is longer than half a wavelength there will be nodes every half wavelength along the string. Since the speed (p.10) of waves in a string is $(T/\mu)^{1/2}$, where T is the tension (p.224) in the string, and μ is the mass per metre length of the string, the frequency of a standing wave can be increased by increasing the tension, or by using a thinner string, or one made of material of a lower density (p.28).

standing wave

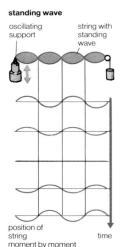

oscillating support

string with standing wave

position of string moment by moment

time

standing waves on a string

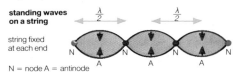

string fixed at each end

$\frac{\lambda}{2}$ $\frac{\lambda}{2}$

N   N   N   N

A   A   A

N = node A = antinode

standing sound waves in a pipe

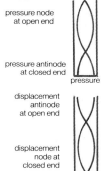

pressure node at open end

pressure antinode at closed end

pressure

displacement antinode at open end

displacement node at closed end

displacement

standing sound waves in a pipe at the open end of a pipe there will be a node (↑) in the changes of pressure (p.30) produced by a sound wave (p.42) and an antinode (↑) in the motion of the gas in the pipe. At the closed end there will be an antinode in the pressure changes and a node in the motion of the gas, with the sound waves being reflected (p.45) at both the open and closed ends. A pressure node will be separated from the next pressure node by one half wavelength (p.43), with motion nodes midway between them at pressure antinodes. To support a standing wave, a pipe which is open at both ends, or closed at both ends, must be a length of a whole number of half wavelengths. A pipe which is open at one end and closed at the other must have a length of a whole number of half wavelengths plus a quarter wavelength.

fundamental, harmonic, overtone

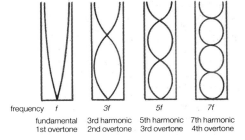

frequency	f	$3f$	$5f$	$7f$
	fundamental	3rd harmonic	5th harmonic	7th harmonic
	1st overtone	2nd overtone	3rd overtone	4th overtone

fundamental[1] (n) the lowest frequency (p.36) standing wave (↑) that can be supported by a system.

harmonic (n) the nth harmonic of a system producing standing waves (↑) is a frequency (p.36) which is n times the fundamental (↑), where n is a whole number.

overtone (n) the nth overtone is the frequency (p.36) of a standing wave (↑) which is the nth frequency of standing wave which the system is able to support, with the fundamental (↑) having a value of $n = 1$, where n is a whole number.

end correction the distance beyond the open end of a pipe at which a sound wave (p.42) appears to be reflected (p.45). The end correction is equal to about 0.6 times the radius of the pipe.

Kundt's tube a way of measuring the wavelength (p.43) of sound. Standing waves (p.52) are set up in a long horizontal glass pipe, along the bottom of which is some fine powder. This powder is moved by the sound wave and settles at the nodes (p.52) in the motion of the gas in the tube, which are half a wavelength apart.

end correction

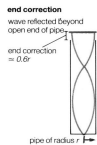

wave reflected beyond open end of pipe

end correction ≃ 0.6r

pipe of radius r

Kundt's tube

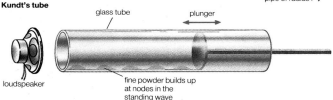

glass tube

plunger

loudspeaker

fine powder builds up at nodes in the standing wave

sonometer (*n*) a stretched metal wire through which an alternating current (p.125) flows. The wire runs between the poles (p.90) of a magnet (p.90). The force on a current carrying wire in a magnetic field (p.92) causes the wire to oscillate (p.35). This starts a standing wave (p.52) with the frequency (p.36) of the alternating current. Standing waves are produced only if the length of the wire is suitable for the wavelength (p.43), and no wave is set up if the magnet is placed at a node (p.52) in the motion of the wire (*see standing waves on a string* (p.52)).

sonometer

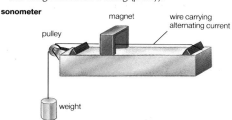

magnet

wire carrying alternating current

pulley

weight

sound

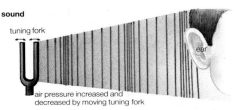

tuning fork

ear

air pressure increased and
decreased by moving tuning fork

sound (*n*) a longitudinal wave (p.43) made up of
areas in a material where the density (p.28), and
pressure (p.30), are higher or lower than normal.
Sound is usually thought of as travelling through
a gas, but it can also travel through solids and
liquids. Such waves can be produced over a
wide range of frequencies (p.36). The range
which can be detected by the human ear is
about 16 Hz to 16 kHz, though the upper end of
this range is often higher in young people.

pitch (*n*) the quality of a sound which depends on
the frequency (p.36) of the sound wave (p.42).
High frequency sound waves are heard as having
a higher pitch than low frequency sound waves.

volume (*n*) the quality of a sound which depends on
the sound wave's (p.42) intensity (p.44). High
intensity sound waves sound louder than low
intensity sound waves. Also known as **loudness**.

loudness (*n*) = volume (↑).

timbre (*n*) the quality of a sound which causes two
sounds of the same pitch (↑) and volume (↑) to
sound different. It depends on the harmonics
(p.53) in the sound wave (p.42), which cause it to
be non-sinusoidal (p.234). The different sounds
produced by different musical instruments are
caused by the different amounts of various
harmonics.

timbre

same frequency,
different timbre

Doppler effect

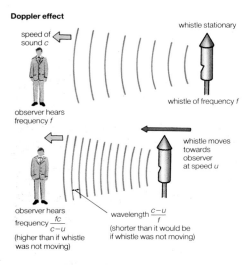

whistle stationary

speed of
sound *c*

observer hears
frequency *f*

whistle of frequency *f*

whistle moves
towards
observer
at speed *u*

observer hears
frequency $\dfrac{fc}{c-u}$
(higher than if whistle
was not moving)

wavelength $\dfrac{c-u}{f}$
(shorter than it would be
if whistle was not moving)

Doppler effect the change in frequency (p.36) of a
sound wave (p.42) heard when the source of the
sound and the listener are moving towards or
away from each other. If the speed of sound is *c*,
the speed of the source towards the listener *u*,
the speed of the listener towards the source *v*,
and the speed of the wind from the source to the
listener *w*, then the frequency heard will be
$(c + w + v)/(c + w - u)$ times the frequency
being produced. If the source and the listener are
moving towards each other, the frequency will
sound higher than it really is; if they are moving
apart, the frequency will sound lower. Any
motion which does not change the distance
between the source and the listener has no
effect. The same effect can be seen in any type
of wave, but the result given here can be used for
electromagnetic waves (p.59) only if the speeds
are much less than the speed of light (p.59)
because of the effects of the special theory of
relativity (p.34).

Doppler shift the change in frequency (p.36)
caused by the Doppler effect (↑).

sonar

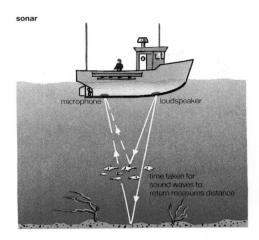

microphone

loudspeaker

time taken for
sound waves to
return measures distance

sonar (*n*) a way of measuring distances, particularly
under water, by measuring the time taken for a
sound wave (p.42) to be reflected (p.45) back
from a distant object, e.g. the seabed.

ultrasound (*n*) sound which is of a frequency
(p.36) above the range of human hearing.
Because of its shorter wavelength (p.43),
ultrasound is diffracted (p.50) less than lower
frequency sound waves (p.42). It is thus used in
sonar (↑) systems for work over smaller
distances, e.g. in testing metal for cracks and for
examining the human body, where it is less
dangerous than X-rays (p.89). **ultrasonic** (*adj*).

decibel (*n*) a unit (p.8) for measuring the volume
(p.55) of sound. It uses a logarithmic scale, so
that a sound of 20dB is ten times louder than
one of 10dB and a sound of 30dB is ten times
louder again. Measurements of loudness in
decibels are usually taken from the threshold of
hearing (↓) as 0dB. **dB** (*abbr*).

threshold of hearing the quietest sound which
can be heard. This varies from person to person,
and with frequency (p.36), but at a frequency of
1kHz it is often taken to be an intensity (p.44) of
$10^{-12}\,\mathrm{W\,m^{-2}}$.

microphone

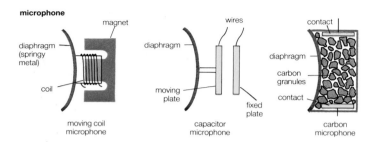

moving coil
microphone

capacitor
microphone

carbon
microphone

microphone (*n*) an instrument for changing sound
energy into electrical energy.

diaphragm (*n*) in a microphone (↑), a springy plate
which is moved by the changing pressure (p.30)
in the sound wave (p.42).

moving coil microphone a microphone (↑) in
which the diaphragm (↑) is fixed to a coil (p.115).
This moves in a magnetic field (p.92), producing
an e.m.f. (p.105) by electromagnetic induction
(p.121).

capacitor microphone a microphone (↑) in which
the diaphragm (↑) is made of metal. This forms
one plate of a capacitor (p.101), the capacitance
(p.101) of which changes as the diaphragm
moves.

carbon microphone a microphone (↑) in which
the diaphragm (↑) presses on grains of carbon.
Changes in the pressure (p.30) on the carbon
change its resistance (p.108).

loudspeaker (*n*) an instrument for changing
electrical energy (p.111) into sound energy.

moving coil loudspeaker a common type of
loudspeaker (↑) in which a current (p.103) flows
through a coil (p.115) supported in a magnetic
field (p.92). The force on a current in a magnetic
field (p.116) starts the coil moving. The coil is fixed
to a stiff cone which moves the air. More than one
size of loudspeaker is needed to cover effectively
the whole frequency (p.36) range that can be
heard by the human ear, so sometimes a large
loudspeaker (called a *woofer*) for low frequencies
is used together with a small loudspeaker (called a
tweeter) for high frequencies.

loudspeaker

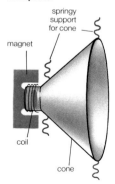

light (*n*) any electromagnetic wave (↓) in the range which can be seen by the human eye, i.e. wavelengths (p.43) of about 4×10^{-7}m to 7×10^{-7}m.

luminous (*adj*) of a body which gives off light of its own. Such bodies can be seen without the use of any other light source.

ray (*n*) an infinitely narrow beam of light, which has parallel (p.234) sides, and which therefore does not spread out.

electromagnetic wave a wave (p.42) in which both an electric field (p.97) and a magnetic field (p.92) are oscillating (p.35). This motion is self-supporting. The changing electric field produces a magnetic field; the changing magnetic field produces an electric field. The electric and magnetic fields are at 90° to each other, and to the direction in which the wave is travelling. In materials in which the wave is not being strongly absorbed (p.242), the oscillations of the electric and magnetic fields are in phase (p.37). All electromagnetic waves travel through a vacuum (p.242) with the same speed (*see speed of light in a vacuum* (↓)). There is no known limit on the wavelength (p.43) of an electromagnetic wave, and waves with wavelengths from several kilometres down to 10^{-14}m are known (*see electromagnetic spectrum* (p.86)). The amount of energy that can be carried by an electromagnetic wave is a multiple of a basic quantum (p.148) of energy, called a photon (p.148). The energy of each photon depends on the frequency (p.36) of the wave. $E = hf$, where E is the energy of a single photon, f is the frequency of the wave, and h is Planck's constant (p.149).

speed of light in a vacuum a fundamental constant (p.234), shown in equations as c. The special theory of relativity (p.34) is based on the fact that the same value for the speed of light will be found whatever the relative velocity (p.11) of the person measuring the speed and of the object producing the light. Theory predicts that $c^2 = (\varepsilon_o \mu_o)^{-1}$, where ε_o is the permittivity of free space (p.98) and μ_o is the permeability of free space (p.114). $c = 2.997\ 924\ 5 \times 10^8$ m s^{-1}

Römer's method for measuring the speed of light

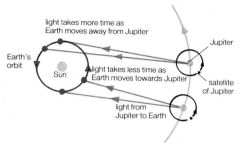

Römer's method for measuring the speed of
light the earliest method of measuring the speed
of light. This made measurements of the times
taken for the satellites (p.26) of the planet (p.26)
Jupiter to complete their orbits (p.26). These
times seemed less when Jupiter was moving
towards the Earth, and more when Jupiter was
moving away from the Earth, because of the time
that the light took to travel from Jupiter to the
Earth.

Fizeau's method for measuring the speed of
light light was passed through spaces in a
toothed wheel before being reflected (p.45) from
a distant mirror. When the light arrived back at
the toothed wheel, it could pass through a gap
between the teeth in the wheel only if the wheel
had moved by an exact number of teeth in the
time the light had taken for its journey.

Fizeau's method for measuring the speed of light

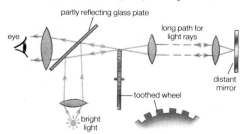

Michelson's method for measuring the speed of light

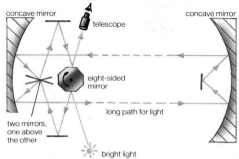

Michelson's method for measuring the speed of light light was reflected (p.45) off an eight-sided mirror, which was turning very quickly. The light was then reflected off a distant mirror before returning to be reflected again at the eight-sided mirror. If the mirror turned through one eighth of a turn in the time that the light took to travel through the apparatus, then the light would appear as it would if the mirror was not turning.

polarization in an electromagnetic wave the direction of polarization (p.101) of an electromagnetic wave (p.59) is taken as being the direction of the electric field (p.97). This is because it is the electric field rather than the magnetic field (p.92) which causes the effects of light on matter.

Polaroid (*n*) a man-made material which allows light with only one direction of polarization (p.101) to pass. Polaroid contains long molecules (p.188) with electrons (p.139) which are free to move along them in an electric field (p.97), and which will take energy from a beam of light. When the material is made, it is stretched to make all these molecules lie in the same direction, so that light of one polarization is absorbed (p.242). This effect works less well at short wavelengths (p.43), so Polaroid is less effective for blue light than for red.

polarization by reflection when unpolarized
(p.43) light hits a transparent (p.62) material, the
light that is reflected (p.45) is partly polarized
(p.43) in the direction parallel to the reflecting
surface. The light that passes into the material,
i.e. the refracted (p.46) ray, is partly polarized in
the direction at 90° to the polarization of the
reflected light. When the refracted ray and the
reflected ray are at 90° to each other, the
reflected light will be completely polarized. The
refracted light is still only partly polarized, with
complete transmission (p.241) of the light
polarized in the direction at 90° to the
polarization of the reflected light.

Brewster angle the angle of incidence (p.45) of
light on a transparent (↓) material at which the
reflected (p.45) and refracted (p.46) rays (p.59)
will be at 90° to each other, with the reflected light
being completely polarized (p.43) (*see polari-
zation by reflection* (↑)). tan $\theta_B = \mu$, where θ_B is the
Brewster angle and μ is the refractive index (p.47).

polarization by reflection

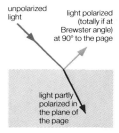

Brewster angle

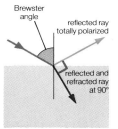

umbra, penumbra

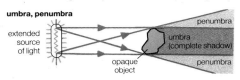

umbra (*n*) the part of a shadow where there is no
light at all. Objects which give out light only from
a small area produce shadows which are mostly
umbra with little penumbra (↓).

penumbra (*n*) the part of a shadow where only
some of the light is stopped by an opaque (↓)
body. Shadows produced by objects giving out
light over a large area may contain only
penumbra, with no umbra (↑).

transparent (*adj*) of a material through which light
can pass with the rays of light being reflected
(p.45) or refracted (p.46) at each surface.

translucent (*adj*) of a material through which light
can pass, but where the light is scattered by the
material.

opaque (*adj*) of a material through which no light
can pass.

spherical mirror

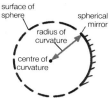

parabolic mirror

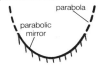

half-silvered mirror a mirror which is made to reflect (p.45) only some of the light that falls on it, allowing the rest to pass through.

spherical mirror a mirror which has a shape like a piece of the surface of a sphere.

radius of curvature the radius of the sphere of which the surface of a spherical mirror (↑) is a part. The radius of curvature of a spherical mirror is twice its focal length (p.64).

centre of curvature the centre of the sphere of which the surface of a spherical mirror (↑) is a part. It is twice as far from the mirror as the principal focus (↓).

parabolic mirror a mirror which has a shape like a parabola (p.234) which has been turned about its axis of symmetry (p.232) to produce a solid surface.

principal axis, principal focus, focal length, concave, convex

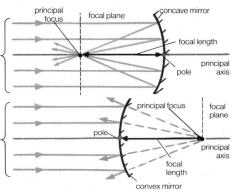

principal axis[1] for a mirror, the line which passes through the centre of a spherical mirror (↑) or parabolic mirror (↑) at 90° to the surface of the mirror.

principal focus[1] (1) in a concave (p.64) mirror, the point through which all rays (p.59) pass, if they were moving parallel to the principal axis (↑) before they hit the mirror; (2) in a convex (p.64) mirror, the point from which all such rays appear to have come.

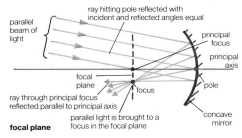

ray hitting pole reflected with
incident and reflected angles equal

parallel beam of light

principal focus

principal axis

focal plane

pole

focus

ray through principal focus
reflected parallel to principal axis

concave mirror

parallel light is brought to a
focus in the focal plane

focal plane

focal plane[1] for a mirror, the plane (p.233) which contains the principal focus (p.63) and which is at 90° to the principal axis (p.63). All rays (p.59) of light in a parallel (p.234) beam will be reflected (p.45) to pass through a single point on the focal plane.

focal length[1] for a mirror, the distance between the centre of a curved mirror and the principal focus (p.63).

pole[1] (*n*) the centre of a curved mirror; the point at which the principal axis (p.63) meets the mirror.

concave (*adj*) of a surface which curves inwards.

convex (*adj*) of a surface which curves outwards.

object (*n*) the thing which is being viewed through a system of lenses (p.68) and/or mirrors.

image (*n*) the coming together of rays (p.59) of light, so that rays which all came from one point on the object (↑) all meet again at one point on the image.

real image an image (↑) where the rays (p.59) of light actually do form an image. If a sheet of white paper was placed at that point, an image would be seen on it.

real image

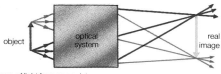

object

optical system

real image

all rays of light from one point
on the object meet at one point
on the image

virtual image

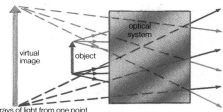

all rays of light from one point
on the object appear to have
come from one point on the image

image in a plane mirror

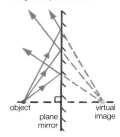

image is same distance behind
mirror as object is in front

virtual (*adj*) of an image (↑) where the rays
(p.59) of light from one point on the object (↑)
do not actually meet at a point on the image.
They only appear to have come from that
point, so that in fact there is nothing actually at
the image point.

image in a plane mirror the image (↑) in a plane
(p.233) mirror is as far behind the mirror as the
object (↑) is in front of it. A line drawn from the
object to the mirror will cross the mirror at 90°.
The image is virtual (↑), the same size as the
object, erect (p.66), and laterally inverted (p.66).

image in a convex mirror the image in a convex
mirror is always erect (p.66), virtual (↑), and with
a magnification (p.67) of less than 1.

image in a convex mirror

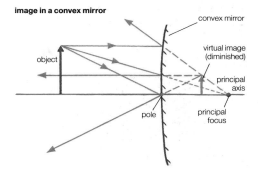

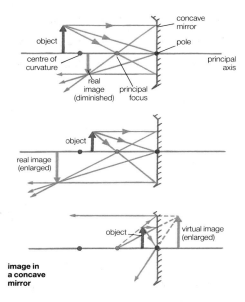

image in
a concave
mirror

image in a concave mirror if the object (p.64) is
closer to the mirror than the principal focus
(p.63), the image will be virtual (p.65), erect (↓),
and with a magnification (↓) of more than 1. If the
object is between the principal focus and the
centre of curvature (p.63), the image will be
inverted (↓), real, and magnified (↓). If the object
is further from the mirror than the centre of
curvature, the image will be inverted, real, and
diminished (↓).

erect (*adj*) of an image (p.64) that is the same way
up as the object (p.64). Also known as **upright**.

upright (*adj*) = erect (↑).

inverted (*adj*) of an image (p.64) which is upside
down, with the top of the object (p.64) appearing
at the bottom of the image.

laterally inverted of an image (p.64) which is back
to front, so that the left-hand side of the object
(p.64) appears on the right-hand side of the
image.

magnification (*n*) the size of the image (p.64) divided by the size of the object (p.64).
magnified (*adj*) having a magnification (↑) of more than 1.
diminished (*adj*) having a magnification (↑) of less than 1.

curved mirror formula

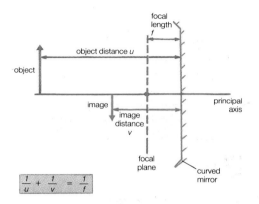

$$\frac{1}{u} + \frac{1}{v} = \frac{1}{f}$$

curved mirror formula if the distance of the object (p.64) from the mirror is *u*, and the distance of the image (p.64) from the mirror is *v*, then $1/u + 1/v = 1/f$, where *f* is the focal length (p.64) of the mirror. Care must be taken about the signs of the numbers (*see real is positive sign convention* (↓)).
real is positive sign convention a way of getting the correct signs in the curved mirror formula (↑), and in the lens formula (p.71). The distance of the object (p.64) from the lens (p.68) or mirror is taken as positive. The distance of the image (p.64) is positive for a real image (p.64) and negative for a virtual (p.65) image. The focal length (pp.64, 69) is positive for a concave (p.64) mirror or a converging (p.68) lens, and negative for a convex (p.64) mirror or a diverging (p.68) lens.

prism

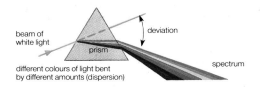

beam of
white light

prism

deviation

spectrum

different colours of light bent
by different amounts (dispersion)

prism (*n*) a piece of glass or other transparent
(p.62) material, having flat faces, usually five in
number, two of them triangular, the others
rectangular.

deviation (*n*) the angle by which a beam of light
changes its path on passing through a prism (↑).

dispersion (*n*) the difference in deviation (↑) for
light of different wavelengths (p.43), due to the
change in refractive index (p.47) with
wavelength. **dispersive** (*adj*).

totally reflecting prism a prism (↑) in which the
light enters at 90° to one face, is totally internally
reflected (p.47) at one or more faces, and then
leaves again at 90° to a face. There is thus no
refraction (p.46) and so no dispersion (↑). Such
prisms are used in place of mirrors in some
optical (p.72) instruments, as they require no
reflective coating.

lens (*n*) a piece of glass or other transparent (p.62)
material, usually in the shape of a circle, with one
or both surfaces being curved, usually in the
shape of part of a sphere.

converging (*adj*) of a lens (↑) which is thicker in
the middle than at the edges, so light rays (p.59)
are brought together by the lens.

diverging (*adj*) of a lens (↑) which is thinner in the
middle than at the edges, so light rays (p.59)
leaving the lens are moving apart from each
other more than they were before entering the
lens.

biconvex (*adj*) of a converging (↑) lens (↑), where
both surfaces are convex (p.64).

plano-convex (*adj*) of a converging (↑) lens (↑),
where one surface is flat and the other convex
(p.64).

totally reflecting prisms

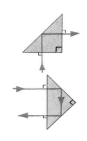

lenses

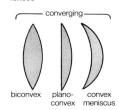

converging

biconvex   plano-
              convex   convex
                          meniscus

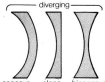

diverging

concave   plano-   biconcave
meniscus   concave

meniscus[1] (*n*) a lens (↑) where one surface is concave (p.64) and the other convex (p.64). Such a lens may be converging (↑) or diverging (↑), depending on which surface is most strongly curved.

biconcave (*adj*) of a diverging (↑) lens (↑), where both surfaces are concave (p.64).

plano-concave (*adj*) of a diverging (↑) lens (↑), where one surface is flat and the other concave (p.64).

optical centre, principal axis, principal focus, focal length

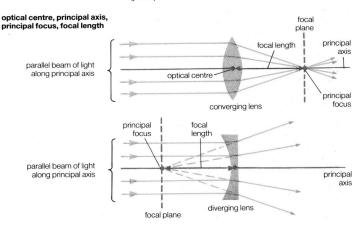

optical centre the thickest point on a converging (↑) lens (↑); the thinnest point on a diverging (↑) lens.

principal axis[2] for a lens (↑), the line passing through the optical centre (↑) of a lens at 90° to the lens.

principal focus[2] (1) for a converging (↑) lens (↑), the point through which all light rays (p.59) pass, if they enter the lens parallel (p.234) to the principal axis (↑); (2) for a diverging (↑) lens, the point from which all such rays appear to have come.

focal length[2] for a lens (↑), the distance from the optical centre (↑) of a lens to the principal focus (↑).

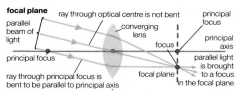

focal plane | ray through optical centre is not bent | principal focus
parallel beam of light | converging lens | principal axis
focus
principal focus | focal plane | parallel light is brought to a focus in the focal plane
ray through principal focus is bent to be parallel to principal axis

focal plane[2] for a lens (p.68), the plane (p.233) at 90° to the principal axis (p.69) which contains the principal focus (p.69). Parallel (p.234) light rays (p.59) will all pass through a point on this plane in a converging (p.68) lens, or will all appear to have come from such a point in a diverging (p.68) lens.

image in a converging lens if an object (p.64) is placed closer to a converging (p.68) lens (p.68) than its focal length (p.69), the image (p.64) will be virtual (p.65), erect (p.65), larger than the object, and further from the lens than the object. If the object is between one and two focal lengths from the lens, the image will be real (p.64), inverted (p.66), larger than the object, and further from the lens than the object. If the distance of the object from the lens is more than twice the focal length, the image will be real, inverted, smaller than the object, and between one and two focal lengths from the lens.

image in a converging lens

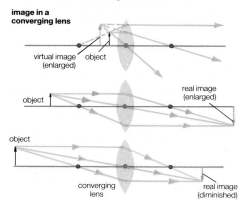

virtual image (enlarged) | object

object | real image (enlarged)

object

converging lens | real image (diminished)

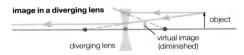

image in a diverging lens

virtual image (diminished)

diverging lens

object

image in a diverging lens the image (p.64) of an object (p.64) in a diverging (p.68) lens (p.68) will always be smaller than the object, erect (p.66) and virtual (p.65).

magnifying glass a converging (p.68) lens (p.68) used with the object (p.64) closer than the focal length (p.69), to form a magnified (p.67), erect (p.66), virtual (p.65) image (p.64).

burning glass an old name for a converging (p.68) lens (p.68), particularly when used to bring together light rays (p.59) from the sun to start a fire.

lens formula

$$\frac{1}{u} + \frac{1}{v} = \frac{1}{f}$$

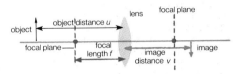

lens formula if the distance of an object (p.64) from a lens (p.68) of focal length (p.69) f is u, and the distance of the image (p.64) is v, then $1/u + 1/v = 1/f$. Care must be taken to give these numbers the correct sign, e.g. by using the real is positive sign convention (p.67).

power of a lens a measure of the ability of a lens (p.68) to bend light. Power $= 1/f$, where f is the focal length (p.69) of the lens.

dioptre, diopter (n) the unit (p.8) in which the power of a lens (p.68) is measured. A lens with a focal length (p.69) of one metre will have a power of one dioptre. Converging (p.68) lenses have positive powers; diverging (p.68) lenses have negative powers.

focus[1] (n) a point where light rays (p.59) come together.

focus[2] (v) (1) of a lens (p.68) or mirror, to bring light rays together; (2) to change the position of parts of an optical (p.72) system to produce a clearer image (p.64).

optics (*n*) the study of light and instruments which depend on light. **optical** (*adj*).

optical lever a way of measuring small movements in a system by shining a beam of light onto a mirror attached to that system.

ray optics that part of optics (↑) which treats light as rays (p.59), travelling in straight lines except when they are reflected (p.45) or refracted (p.46). It takes no account of the wave (p.42) nature of light. Also known as **geometrical optics**.

geometrical optics = ray optics (↑).

wave optics that part of optics (↑) where the wave (p.42) nature of light is important, particularly where light waves interfere (p.48) or diffract (p.50).

telescope (*n*) any instrument which makes far away objects appear closer.

astronomical telescope a telescope (↑) used to look at stars or planets (p.26). Such telescopes are usually simple in form, though they may be very large. They produce images (p.64) which are inverted (p.66).

terrestrial telescope a telescope (↑) used to look at objects on the Earth. In such an instrument an inverted (p.66) image (p.64) is a serious problem, so terrestrial telescopes are made to produce erect (p.66) images.

reflecting telescope a telescope (↑) in which the light entering the telescope is focused (p.71) by a mirror rather than a lens (p.68). Most modern astronomical telescopes (↑) are of this type.

Newtonian telescope a form of reflecting telescope (↑). The light entering the telescope is focused (p.71) by a large curved mirror. It is then reflected (p.45) out of the telescope by a small flat mirror to form a real image (p.64). This image is then magnified (p.67) by a small converging (p.68) lens (p.68) of short focal length (p.69).

primary mirror the large, concave (p.64) mirror in a reflecting telescope (↑).

secondary mirror a small mirror in a reflecting telescope (↑). Light hits this mirror after it has been reflected (p.45) off the primary mirror (↑). The secondary mirror may be flat or curved, depending on the type of telescope.

Newtonian telescope

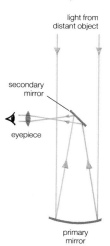

light from distant object

secondary mirror

eyepiece

primary mirror

refracting telescope (astronomical)

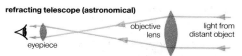

refracting telescope a telescope (↑) in which
light entering the telescope is focused (p.71)
using a lens (p.68) rather than a mirror. Light
enters the telescope through a large
converging (p.68) lens. In the astronomical (↑)
form of refracting telescope the image (p.64)
formed by the first lens is viewed through a
short focal length (p.69) converging lens. In a
terrestrial telescope (↑), either a third
converging lens is used in order to turn the
image the right way up, or a diverging (p.68)
lens is placed just inside the principal focus
(p.69) of the object glass (↓), in order to form a
distant, virtual (p.65) image which appears
larger than the object.

object glass the lens (p.68) through which light
enters a refracting telescope (↑) or a compound
microscope (p.75). Also known as **objective
lens**.

objective lens = object glass (↑).

Galilean telescope a terrestrial telescope (↑) with
a converging (p.68) lens (p.68) for an object
glass (↑) and a diverging (p.68) lens for an eye
lens.

magnification of a telescope the angle taken up
by the image (p.64) divided by the angle taken up
by the object (p.64). This is equal to the focal
length (p.69) of the object glass (↑) in a refracting
telescope (↑), or of the primary mirror (↑) in a
reflecting telescope (↑), divided by the focal
length of the eye lens.

magnification of a telescope

$$\text{magnification} = \frac{a_2}{a_1} = \frac{f_1}{f_2}$$

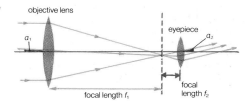

resolving power of a telescope

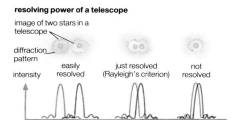

image of two stars in a
telescope

diffraction
pattern

intensity   easily
resolved

just resolved
(Rayleigh's criterion)

not
resolved

resolving power of a telescope the ability of a
telescope (p.72) to show two objects (p.64) as
being two separate objects rather than one. This
does not depend simply on the magnification
(p.73) of the telescope. Each point on an object
will appear on the image (p.64) not as a point but
as a diffraction pattern (p.51) produced as the
light enters the telescope. If there is enough
magnification, Rayleigh's criterion ($\downarrow$) can be
used. The smallest angle between two objects
for them to be separated by a telescope with an
object glass (p.73) or a primary mirror (p.72) of
diameter D is $1.22\lambda/D$, where λ is the
wavelength (p.43) of the light used. This is one
reason why astronomical telescopes (p.72) are
made as large as possible. Another is the ability
of a large instrument to collect more light from
faint objects.

resolve (v) to be able to tell whether there are two
objects (p.64) very close together, rather than a
single object. **resolution** (n).

Rayleigh's criterion an optical (p.72) instrument
will just be able to resolve ($\uparrow$) two objects (p.64)
of equal brightness if the centre of the diffraction
pattern (p.51) formed by one of the objects lies
on top of the first dark ring in the diffraction
pattern of the second object.

microscope (n) any instrument which produces
an image (p.64) which is larger than the small
object (p.64) being viewed.

simple microscope a microscope ($\uparrow$) which uses
a single converging (p.68) lens (p.68) as a
magnifying glass (p.71).

compound microscope

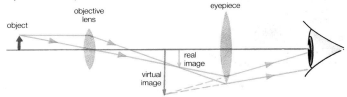

condenser

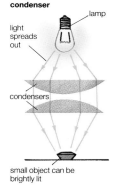

compound microscope a microscope (↑) which uses one converging (p.68) lens (p.68) to form a real image (p.64) which is larger than the object (p.64). This is viewed through a second converging lens which acts as a magnifying glass (p.71).

condenser[1] (*n*) a thick converging (p.68) lens (p.68) used to collect light from a lamp and focus (p.71) it onto a small area, making the light brighter in that area.

eye (*n*) the part of an animal which is sensitive to light. In mammals, the front of the eye is curved to refract (p.46) light. The light then passes through a converging (p.68) lens (p.68) and is further refracted. This lens can be made fatter or thinner by muscles, so the eye can form clear images (p.64) of objects (p.64) at different distances. The image is formed on the retina (p.76) at the back of the eye.

cornea (*n*) the transparent (p.62) curved part of the eye (↑) through which light enters.

ciliary muscles the muscles which change the shape of the lens (p.68) in the eye (↑).

eye

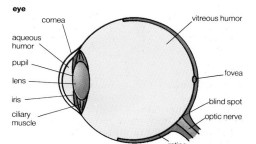

accommodation (*n*) the act of an eye (p.75) in forming clear images (p.64) of objects (p.64) at different distances.

pupil (*n*) the part of the front of the eye (p.75) through which light passes. It appears black since there is much less light inside the eye than outside.

retina (*n*) the light-detecting area at the back of the eye (p.75),on which an image (p.64) is formed.

blind spot that part of the retina (↑) where the optic nerve (↓) enters. The retina does not detect light at this point.

optic nerve the nerve which carries information from the retina (↑) to the brain.

persistence of vision the eye (p.75) is not able to detect very quick changes in an object (p.64), so a series of still pictures seen rapidly one after another will appear as a smoothly moving picture.

longsighted (*adj*) of someone whose eye (p.75) has a lens (p.68) too weak to form images (p.64) of close objects (p.64). This can be changed using a converging (p.68) lens in front of the eye.

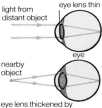

accommodation

light from distant object — eye lens thin

eye

nearby object

eye lens thickened by pressure from ciliary muscles

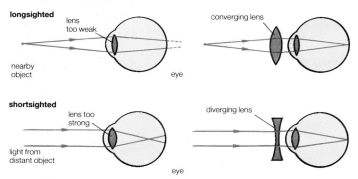

longsighted

lens too weak

nearby object

eye

converging lens

shortsighted

lens too strong

light from distant object

eye

diverging lens

shortsighted (*adj*) of someone whose eye (p.75) has a lens (p.68) too strong to form images (p.64) of distant objects (p.64). This can be changed using a diverging (p.68) lens in front of the eye. Also known as **myopic**.

myopic (*adj*) = shortsighted (↑).

Young's double slit experiment

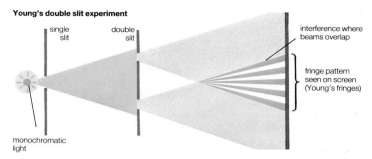

single slit

double slit

interference where beams overlap

fringe pattern seen on screen (Young's fringes)

monochromatic light

Young's double slit experiment an experiment to show the interference (p.48) of two beams of light. A narrow area of monochromatic (p.82) light, e.g. a slit lit by a filament lamp (p.82) with a coloured filter (p.83), a laser (p.82) or a sodium vapour lamp (p.82), shines light onto two narrow slits. Light from these slits spreads out because of diffraction (p.50). Where the two beams meet, they interfere, producing bright areas where there is constructive (p.48) interference, and dark areas where there is destructive (p.49) interference. The pattern is more widely spaced if light of a longer wavelength (p.43) is used, or if the pattern is viewed further from the double slits or if the double slits are closer together. The spacing between one bright area and the next is $\lambda D/d$, where λ is the wavelength, D the distance from the slits to the point where the pattern is viewed, and d the distance between the two slits.

Young's fringes the pattern of light and dark lines that are seen in Young's double slit experiment (↑).

Young's fringes in white light since white light contains different wavelengths (p.43) mixed together, if Young's double slit experiment (↑) is performed with white light, a series of Young's fringes (↑) can be seen with different colours and different separations. After a short distance the different patterns become so disordered that no pattern of light and dark lines can be seen.

Fresnel's biprism experiment

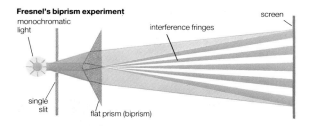

monochromatic
light

interference fringes

screen

single
slit

flat prism (biprism)

Fresnel's biprism experiment a form of Young's
double slit experiment (p.77) in which the slits are
changed for a single slit and a very flat prism
(p.68) (called a biprism). Light passing through
the slit is diffracted (p.50) onto different parts of
the prism. Light which passes through different
faces of the prism is refracted (p.46) differently,
and seems to come from different points. The
light beams from the two faces of the prism
interfere (p.48), producing a pattern of light and
dark lines.

Lloyd's mirror experiment a form of Young's
double slit experiment (p.77) in which the slits are
changed for a single slit and a flat mirror at 90° to
the slit. Light spreads out from the single slit by
diffraction (p.50), and light which has been
reflected (p.45) by the mirror interferes (p.48)
with that which has not. Because of the 180°
phase change on reflection at the mirror (*see
phase change on reflection* (p.47)), the areas
which were dark in the Young's double slit
experiment are now bright, and the bright areas
are now dark.

Lloyd's mirror experiment

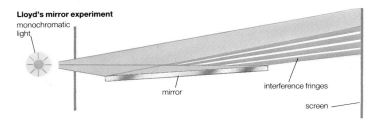

monochromatic
light

mirror

interference fringes

screen

thin film interference

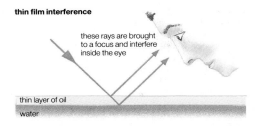

these rays are brought
to a focus and interfere
inside the eye

thin layer of oil

water

thin film interference interference (p.48) between
two beams of light which have been reflected
(p.45) off opposite surfaces of a thin layer of air,
oil or other material. If the thickness of the layer
changes, the phase difference (p.37) between
the two light waves (p.42) will change, and so will
the pattern of constructive (p.48) and destructive
(p.49) interference. This can be used to measure
the thickness of the layer or the flatness of one of
the surfaces.

Newton's rings a pattern of thin film interference
(p.48) which results from the interference
between light that has been reflected (p.45) off
the bottom surface of a converging (p.68) lens
(p.68) and light that has been reflected off the
top surface of a flat piece of glass on which the
lens stands.

Newton's rings

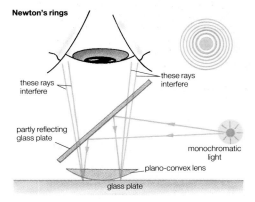

these rays
interfere

these rays
interfere

partly reflecting
glass plate

monochromatic
light

plano-convex lens

glass plate

spectrometry (*n*) the study of spectra (↓). Also known as **spectroscopy**.

spectroscopy (*n*) = spectrometry (↑).

spectrum (*n*) the light given off by some object, separated by wavelength (p.43), so light with different wavelengths, i.e. different colours, appears in different places on the spectrum. **spectra** (*pl*).

spectrometer (*n*) an instrument for separating light of different wavelengths (p.43) to produce a spectrum (↑) and to measure the wavelengths present.

diffraction grating a piece of material having a very large number of parallel lines on it. The lines are evenly and closely spaced. When light falls on the grating, each of the spaces between the lines scatters the light, and the light from these spaces interferes (p.48). In most directions there will be destructive (p.49) interference, but in those directions where the light leaving one space is exactly in phase (p.37) with that from the next, all the beams of light will interfere constructively (p.48). The directions of constructive interference will be different for light of different wavelengths (p.43), so a diffraction grating separates light according to its wavelength. If the light hits the grating at 90° to its surface, it will leave the grating in those directions where $d\sin\theta = n\lambda$, where d is the distance between the lines on the grating, λ is the wavelength of the light, θ is the angle to the normal (p.234) to the grating, and n is a whole number. For wavelengths which do not pass through glass, a reflection grating is used in which light enters and leaves the grating from the same side rather than passing through the grating.

order (*n*) the whole number n in the diffraction grating (↑) equation.

grating spectrometer a spectrometer (↑) which uses a diffraction grating (↑). It also contains a collimator (↓) and a telescope (p.72) to bring together the parallel light rays (p.59) leaving the grating. The telescope can be moved to different angles to collect light leaving the grating in different directions.

diffraction grating

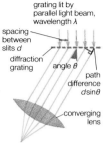

grating lit by parallel light beam, wavelength λ

spacing between slits *d*

diffraction grating

angle θ

path difference *d*sinθ

converging lens

beams interfere constructively if $d\sin\theta = n\lambda$

grating spectrometer

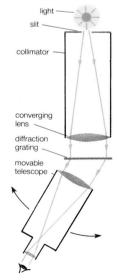

light

slit

collimator

converging lens

diffraction grating

movable telescope

collimator (*n*) an instrument for producing a parallel (p.234) beam of light. It contains a narrow slit through which the light passes and spreads out by diffraction (p.50). The slit is placed in the focal plane (p.70) of a converging (p.68) lens (p.68).

line spectrum a spectrum (↑) in which only a few very small ranges of wavelength (p.43) are present, in an emission spectrum (↓), or absent, in an absorption spectrum (↓). Such spectra are produced by changes in the positions of electrons (p.139) in atoms (p.139), and usually have wavelengths in the visible (p.88), ultra-violet (p.89) or X-ray (p.89) parts of the electromagnetic spectrum (p.86).

band spectrum a spectrum (↑) in which large ranges of wavelength (p.43) are present, in an emission spectrum (↓), or absent, in an absorption spectrum (↓). They are caused by changes in the motion of molecules (p.188), and usually have wavelengths in the infra-red (p.88) or visible (p.88) parts of the electromagnetic spectrum (p.86).

emission spectrum a spectrum (↑) which is produced by making the material being examined give off its own light, e.g. by passing an electric current (p.103) through a gas.

absorption spectrum a spectrum (↑) which is produced by shining a wide range of wavelengths (p.43), e.g. white light from a filament lamp (p.82), through the material being examined and seeing which wavelengths do not pass through the material.

resolving power of a spectrometer the ability of a spectrometer (↑) to separate two very similar wavelengths (p.43). In a grating spectrometer (↑), the wider the grating the better the resolving power, since if a wavelength is not of quite the right size to satisfy $d\sin\theta = n\lambda$, a wider grating will produce more beams of light to cancel each other out. The resolving power of a spectrometer is also reduced if the slit in the collimator (↑) is too wide. Two wavelengths, λ and λ', will just be separated if $\lambda/(\lambda - \lambda') = Nn$, where n is the order (↑) of the spectrum and N is the number of lines on the diffraction grating (↑).

emission spectrum

absorption spectrum

band spectrum

monochromatic (*adj*) containing light of only one wavelength (p.43).

filament lamp a light which works by passing a current (p.103) though a thin wire (called a *filament*) with a high melting point (p.192). The filament is usually made of tungsten. This produces a wide range of wavelengths (p.43) in the infra-red (p.88) and visible (p.88) parts of the electromagnetic spectrum (p.86).

filament (*n*) a very fine thread or wire, particularly a wire which is heated by passing a current (p.103) through it.

sodium vapour lamp a light which works by passing a current (p.103) through vapour (p.195) of the metal sodium. The emission spectrum (p.81) of sodium has two very bright lines with very similar wavelengths (p.43) of about 589nm. For many purposes this can be used as a monochromatic (↑) light source.

laser (*abbr*) *l*ight *a*mplification by *s*timulated *e*mission of *r*adiation. A machine which produces a very bright, monochromatic (↑) light. This light is also very coherent (p.49) and can be made to give a very nearly parallel beam. A laser operates by causing many atoms (p.139) to make transitions (p.143) from one excited (p.143) state to another, or to their ground state (p.143), in such a way that all the photons (p.148) produced are in phase (p.37). This process is called *stimulated emission*. Many materials can be made to lase, giving off light of various wavelengths, e.g. carbon dioxide (infra-red (p.88)), helium-neon mixture (red). **lase** (*v*).

hologram

reference beam

photographic plate (hologram)

diverging lens

half-silvered mirror

laser

light scattered off object interferes with reference beam

object

hologram (*n*) a way of storing a solid image (p.64) on a flat plate. The object (p.64) to be photographed is lit by coherent (p.49) light from a laser (↑). The light reflected (p.45) from the object is made to interfere (p.48) with a beam of light direct from the laser, and the pattern of light and dark areas formed by this interference is stored photographically.

colour[1] (*n*) the effect of the eye separating different wavelengths (p.43) of light. As the wavelength of light moves from the longest visible (p.88) to the shortest visible, the colours red, orange, yellow, green, blue, indigo (blue/purple) and violet are seen. White light is made up of a roughly equal mixture of these colours, so when white light is refracted (p.46) in a prism (p.68) or a rainbow (p.88), dispersion (p.68) causes these same colours to be produced. A second prism can bring these colours together again to make white light.

Richard of York gave battle in vain a method of remembering the order of the colours (↑) from the longest to the shortest wavelength (p.43).

primary colour any of the three colours red, green or blue. A mixture of suitable amounts of light in these colours can produce the appearance of any other colour.

secondary colour any of the three colours that remain when one of the primary colours (↑) is taken away from white light, or that are made by mixing equal amounts of light of two of the primary colours. They are yellow, cyan (blue/green) and magenta (red/purple).

filter (*n*) a piece of material which allows light of certain colours to pass, but not others. E.g. a red filter allows through only red light, so white light shone onto a red filter comes out as red, but if blue light is shone on a red filter, no light will pass through the filter.

filter

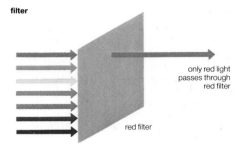

only red light
passes through
red filter

red filter

additive mixing of colours
red, green and blue patches of
light on a white screen

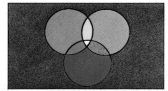

subtractive mixing of colours
white light seen through cyan,
magenta and yellow filters

additive mixing of colours the mixing of colours,
usually primary colours (p.83), to produce other
colours by adding light of one colour to light of
another colour; e.g. yellow can be made by
adding red and green light.

subtractive mixing of colours the mixing
of colours by starting with white light, i.e.
all colours, and taking away the unwanted
colours.

colours of objects viewed in coloured light
objects seen in coloured light can only reflect
(p.45) the colours in the light in which they are
viewed. E.g. a white object seen in green light will
seem green as it reflects all light that falls on it. A
green object seen in green light also appears
green, as it reflects green light, but a red object
seen in green light will appear black. It will reflect
any red light that falls on it but since there is none
it reflects no light, and so seems black.

colours of objects viewed in coloured light

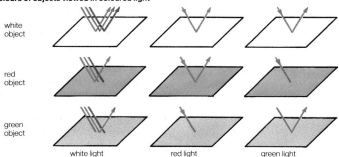

colour television

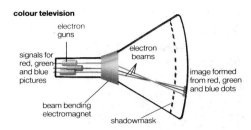

electron guns

signals for red, green and blue pictures

electron beams

image formed from red, green and blue dots

beam bending electromagnet

shadowmask

rainbow

white light from sun

raindrop

complementary colours

primary colours

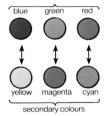

blue   green   red

yellow   magenta   cyan

secondary colours

colour television pictures formed using a special cathode ray tube (p.137) which has three electron guns (p.136). Near the front of the tube there is a metal sheet with holes in it called a *shadowmask*; the holes are placed so that electrons (p.139) from each of the three guns can only fall on one of the three types of material coating the front of the tube, which give out red, green or blue light when struck by electrons. Thus each electron gun produces a picture in red, green or blue light, and additive mixing of colours (p.83) produces the appearance of a fully coloured picture.

rainbow (*n*) a pattern produced when raindrops refract (p.46) light from the sun. The light is totally internally reflected (p.47) and refracted as it leaves the drop. Further reflection (p.45) of light inside the drop may produce a second, fainter, rainbow.

complementary colour the colour that remains when a certain colour has been removed from white light; e.g. magenta (red/purple) is the complementary colour to green.

colour-blindness (*n*) a condition in which a person is unable to see the difference between certain colours, e.g. red and green. It is caused by a fault in the retina (p.76).

secondary yellow the yellow colour which is seen on mixing red and green light. If this yellow light is passed through a spectrometer (p.80), it would again be separated into red and green, unlike pure yellow light of a single wavelength (p.43), though in fact the eye is unable to tell them apart.

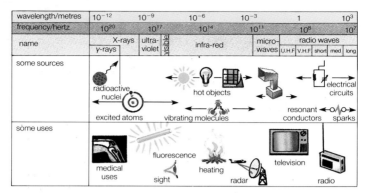

wavelength/metres	10^{-12}	10^{-9}	10^{-6}	10^{-3}	1	10^3
frequency/hertz	10^{20}	10^{17}	10^{14}	10^{11}	10^8	10^7

electromagnetic spectrum the range of different frequencies (p.36) or wavelengths (p.43) of electromagnetic waves (p.59).

electromagnetic
spectrum

radio wave an electromagnetic wave (p.59) with a frequency (p.36) less than about 3×10^{11}Hz, i.e. a wavelength (p.43) more than about 10^{-3}m. The waves are produced by making an oscillating (p.35) electric current (p.103) flow in an aerial ($\downarrow$), and are detected by the currents they cause in other aerials. Information can be carried on the waves by modulation (p.50).

long wave a radio wave ($\uparrow$) having a wavelength (p.43) more than about 10^3m, i.e. a frequency less than about 3×10^5Hz.

medium wave a radio wave ($\uparrow$) having a wavelength (p.43) between about 10^3m and 10^2m, i.e. a frequency between about 3×10^5Hz and 3×10^6Hz.

short wave a radio wave ($\uparrow$) having a wavelength (p.43) between about 10^2m and 10m, i.e. a frequency (p.36) between about 3×10^6Hz and 3×10^7Hz. These waves are sometimes reflected (p.45) off an ionized (p.139) layer in the upper atmosphere (p.31), and so can be used to send messages around the world without using man-made satellites (p.26).

ionosphere (*n*) the ionized (p.139) layer in the upper atmosphere (p.31) off which radio waves ($\uparrow$) are sometimes reflected (p.45).

radar

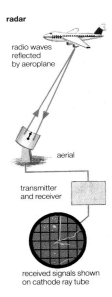

radio waves
reflected
by aeroplane

aerial

transmitter
and receiver

received signals shown
on cathode ray tube

aerial

very high frequency of radio waves (↑) having a
wavelength (p.43) between about 10m and 1m,
i.e. a frequency (p.36) between about 3 x 10⁷Hz
and 3 x 10⁸Hz. These waves are not usually
reflected by the ionosphere (↑), so are used for
short range radio systems and for carrying
messages to and from man-made satellites
(p.26). **V.H.F.** (*abbr*).

ultra high frequency of radio waves (↑) with
wavelengths (p.43) less than about 1m, i.e.
frequencies (p.36) higher than about 3 x 10⁸Hz.
These frequencies are used for television and
radar (↓). **U.H.F.** (*abbr*).

radar (*n*) a way of finding objects and measuring
their distance by measuring the time for a radio
wave (↑) to return to an aerial (↓) after it has been
reflected (p.45) off a distant object. By looking at
the Doppler shift (p.56) of the reflected radio
wave, the object's speed can also be measured.

aerial (*n*) a wire made to send or receive radio
waves (↑). At lower frequencies (p.36), a simple
wire of a similar length to the wavelength (p.43)
of the waves is often used, but at higher
frequencies a system of conductors (p.96) is
used to shape the waves into a narrow beam or
to increase the ability to detect waves coming
from a certain direction. Also known as **antenna**.

antenna (*n*) = aerial (↑).

directional (*adj*) of an aerial which sends or
receives radio waves (↑) only in certain directions.

microwave (*n*) an electromagnetic wave (p.59)
with a wavelength (p.43) between about 10^{-1}
and 10^{-4}m, i.e. a frequency (p.36) between
about 3 x 10⁹Hz and 3 x 10¹²Hz. They are used
for radar (↑) and short distance radio systems as
well as for cooking food (*see heating effect of
microwaves* (↓)).

heating effect of microwaves microwaves (↑) of
certain frequencies (p.36) can be used to heat
objects containing water, particularly food, by
choosing the microwave frequency equal to one of
the natural frequencies (p.40) of oscillation (p.35)
of water molecules (p.188). The microwaves then
set the molecules oscillating, and the energy
spreads through the object as heat energy (p.18).

infra-red (*adj*) of electromagnetic radiation (p.241)
with wavelengths (p.43) in the range about 10^{-4}m
to 7×10^{-7}m, i.e. frequencies (p.36) in the range
about 3×10^{12}Hz to 4×10^{14}Hz. Infra-red
radiation is given off by all hot objects, and can be
detected by its heating effect on objects which
absorb (p.242) it. Dull, dark surfaces are strong
absorbers of infra-red radiation, so a
thermometer (p.182) with a blackened bulb (*see
liquid in glass thermometer* (p.182)) can be used
to detect infra-red radiation, as can a bolometer
($\downarrow$). **I.R.** (*abbr*).

black body radiation the spectrum (p.80) of
electromagnetic radiation (p.241) given off by an
object which would absorb (p.242) completely
any electromagnetic radiation of any frequency
(p.36) falling on it (and so is completely black). The
wavelength (p.43) at which the most energy is
given off is inversely proportional (p.235) to the
absolute temperature (p.184) of the object. If an
object is hot enough, it may give off visible ($\downarrow$)
light. The colour of this light changes from red to
orange to white to blue as the temperature
increases.

Stefan's law the amount of power (p.19) produced
in black body radiation ($\uparrow$) is equal to $A\sigma T^4$, where
A is the area of the surface of the object, T is the
absolute temperature (p.184) of the object, and σ
is the Stefan-Boltzmann constant ($\downarrow$).

Stefan-Boltzmann constant the constant (p.234)
σ in Stefan's law ($\uparrow$), $\sigma = 5.7 \times 10^{-8}$ W m^{-2}K^{-4}.

bolometer (*n*) an instrument for detecting infra-red
($\uparrow$) electromagnetic waves (p.59). It is made from
a strip of platinum metal, painted black to absorb
the energy most effectively. The strip is heated by
the energy and its electrical resistance (p.108)
increases.

visible (*adj*) of electromagnetic radiation (p.241)
which can be detected by human eyes. This has a
wavelength (p.43) in the range 7×10^{-7}m to
4×10^{-7}m, i.e. a frequency (p.36) between about
4×10^{14}Hz and 7×10^{14}Hz. Visible light is given
off by very hot objects, including the sun, and by
changes in the arrangements of electrons (p.139)
in atoms (p.139).

infra-red

infra-red radiation

hot object
(electric heater)

thermometers
dark object absorbs more
infra-red radiation

black body radiation

intensity of
radiation

increasing
temperature

wavelength

bolometer

blackened platinum strip

insulating support

fluorescent

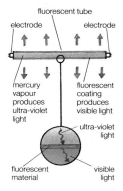

fluorescent tube

electrode — electrode

mercury vapour produces ultra-violet light

fluorescent coating produces visible light

ultra-violet light

fluorescent material

visible light

ultra-violet (*adj*) of electromagnetic waves (p.59) which have a wavelength (p.43) between 4×10^{-7}m and about 10^{-8}m, i.e. a frequency (p.36) between 7×10^{14}Hz and about 3×10^{16}Hz. Ultra-violet light is given off by changes in the arrangements of electrons (p.139) in atoms (p.139), and by the very hottest objects, e.g. stars. In large quantities ultra-violet light can cause enough ionization (p.139) to be dangerous to life.

fluorescent (*adj*) of a material which gives off visible (↑) light when hit by electromagnetic waves (p.59) of a shorter wavelength (p.43) than visible light. The energy of the electromagnetic wave is taken in and then given out in two or more smaller steps, at least one of which produces visible light.

X-ray (*n*) an electromagnetic wave (p.59) with a wavelength (p.43) shorter than about 10^{-8}m, i.e. a frequency (p.36) greater than about 3×10^{16}Hz. X-rays are given off by changes in the arrangements of electrons (p.139) in atoms (p.139), where each element (p.139) produces its own line spectrum (p.81) of X-rays. X-rays are also produced when electrons are violently accelerated (p.12) or slowed down, as in an X-ray tube (↓). This produces X-rays with a wider spread of wavelengths. X-rays will pass through all but the densest (p.28) materials and so are used to examine the inside of objects. They also cause a certain amount of ionization (p.139), with the result that they can be dangerous to life.

X-ray tube an evacuated (p.242) container with a filament (p.82) which gives off electrons (p.139) by thermionic emission (p.135), and an anode (p.113) which is made of a large piece of metal in order to conduct (p.96) away the heat produced. There is a potential difference (p.107) of at least 20kV between the anode and the filament, so electrons hit the anode at great speed. The higher the potential difference used, the faster the electrons are moving when they reach the anode, and the shorter the wavelength (p.43) of the shortest wavelength X-rays (↑) produced.

X-ray tube

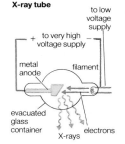

to low voltage supply

to very high voltage supply

metal anode

filament

evacuated glass container

X-rays

electrons

magnet (*n*) any object which produces a magnetic field (p.92), particularly a bar or U-shaped piece of ferromagnetic (p.93) material. **magnetic** (*adj*), **magnetism** (*n*), **magnetize** (*v*).

pole[2] (*n*) the area on a magnet (↑) where magnetic flux lines (p.92) enter or leave the magnet.

north and south seeking poles the two poles (↑) of a simple magnet (↑). If such a magnet is free to turn, one end will point towards the magnetic north pole (↓). This is the north seeking pole; the other end is the south seeking pole.

magnetic north and south poles the points on the surface of the Earth where the magnetic flux lines (p.92) from the Earth's magnetic field (p.92) are at 90° to the Earth's surface. The magnetic north pole is in the northern half of the Earth and is a south seeking pole (↑). These points are close to the axis (p.26) about which the Earth turns. The position of the magnetic poles changes slowly with time.

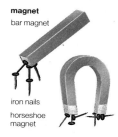

magnet
bar magnet

iron nails
horseshoe magnet

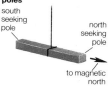

north and south seeking poles
south seeking pole
north seeking pole
to magnetic north

magnetic compass
scale
magnet
case
pivot

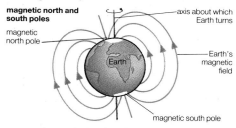

magnetic north and south poles
magnetic north pole
axis about which Earth turns
Earth
Earth's magnetic field
magnetic south pole

magnetic north the direction to the magnetic north pole (↑).

magnetic compass a compass which uses the Earth's magnetic field (p.92) to show the direction of the Earth's magnetic north and south poles (↑).

plotting compass a small magnetic compass (↑) used to find the direction of a magnetic field (p.92).

angle of dip the angle between the Earth's magnetic flux lines (p.92) and the surface of the Earth.

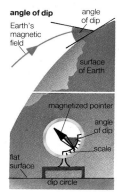

angle of dip
angle of dip
Earth's magnetic field
surface of Earth
magnetized pointer
angle of dip
scale
flat surface
dip circle

magnetic variation

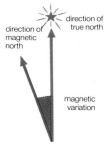

direction of true north

direction of magnetic north

magnetic variation

domain

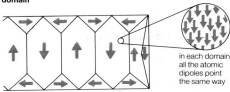

in each domain all the atomic dipoles point the same way

induced magnetism

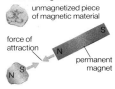

unmagnetized piece of magnetic material

force of attraction

permanent magnet

induced magnetism

demagnetization

a.c. solenoid
1

hammering
2

heating
3

magnetic variation the angle between the direction to the magnetic north pole (↑) and true north. It varies from place to place and over time.

domain (*n*) an area in a ferromagnetic (p.93) material in which all the magnetic dipoles (p.93) point in the same direction.

permanent magnet a magnet (↑) which always has a magnetic field (p.92), i.e. one made of a ferromagnetic (p.93) material in which the domains (↑) are kept pointing in the same direction by the forces they produce on one another, rather than by the effect of some outside magnetic field.

induced magnetism magnetism (↑) of one object caused by a magnetic field (p.92) produced by another. An unmagnetized ferromagnetic (p.93) material may have its domains (↑) lined up by a magnetic field (p.92), and will then produce a magnetic field of its own. This may or may not remain when the magnetizing field is taken away, depending on the forces between the domains.

demagnetization (*n*) the taking away of a magnetic field (p.92) from a ferromagnetic (p.93) material. This can be done by placing the material in an alternating (p.240) magnetic field, which is gradually reduced, taking the material around smaller and smaller hysteresis loops (p.94). Materials can also be demagnetized by heating to a temperature (p.181) above the Curie point (↓), or by hammering. Both these methods destroy the ordering of the domains (↑).

Curie point the temperature (p.181) above which the vibration (p.242) of the atoms (p.139) in a ferromagnetic (p.93) material is fast enough to destroy the ordering of the domains (↑) in the material.

magnetic field the effect of a magnet (p.90) on objects around it. The strength of the magnetic field at a point is a measure of the effect that the magnet will have at that point.

tesla (*n*) the SI unit (p.8) of magnetic field (↑). A field of one tesla will produce a force of one newton (p.14) on each metre of a wire carrying a current (p.103) of one amp (p.103) at 90° to the field (*see force on a current in a magnetic field* (p.116)). **T** (*abbr*).

magnetic flux the number of magnetic flux lines (↓) passing through a given area. If the magnetic field (↑) is *B*, and the area is *A*, and the angle between the magnetic field and the normal (p.234) to the area is θ, $\phi = BA\cos\theta$, where ϕ is the magnetic flux.

weber (*n*) the SI unit (p.8) of magnetic flux (↑). A magnetic field (↑) of one tesla (↑), at 90° to an area of one square metre, produces a flux of one weber. **Wb** (*abbr*).

magnetic flux lines lines drawn to show the direction of a magnetic field (↑) at any point. The direction of the magnetic flux lines can be found using a plotting compass (p.90) or small needle-shaped particles of iron (which are called *iron filings*).

neutral point any point in a magnetic (p.90) system where there is no magnetic field (↑). A neutral point is produced where the magnetic fields from two or more magnetic poles (p.90) are in opposite directions, e.g. between two magnets (p.90) with their north seeking poles (p.90) placed close to each other.

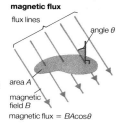

magnetic flux

flux lines

angle θ

area *A*

magnetic field *B*

magnetic flux = $BA\cos\theta$

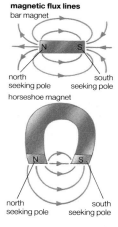

magnetic flux lines

bar magnet

north seeking pole

south seeking pole

horseshoe magnet

north seeking pole

south seeking pole

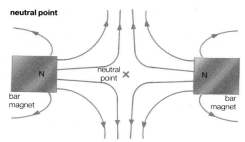

neutral point

bar magnet

neutral point ×

bar magnet

magnetic dipole

bar magnet

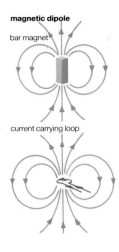

current carrying loop

paramagnetic

each atom behaves like a magnetic dipole

no magnetic field

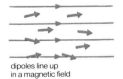

dipoles line up
in a magnetic field

ferromagnetic

all atomic dipoles lined up

magnetic dipole the simplest form of magnet (p.90), having a north seeking and a south seeking pole (p.90). At large distances compared to the size of the magnet itself, the magnetic field (↑) is inversely proportional (p.235) to the third power of the distance from the magnet. A loop of wire carrying a current (p.103) also produces a magnetic field which is the same as the long distance dipole field if the distance from the loop is large compared to its radius.

magnetic moment a measure of the strength of a magnetic dipole (↑). It is equal to the largest couple (p.26) that can be produced on the dipole by a magnetic field (↑) of one tesla (↑). For a current (p.103) carrying loop, the magnetic moment is also equal to the current multiplied by the area of the loop. SI unit (p.8): Am^2.

diamagnetic (*adj*) of a material whose atoms (p.139) or molecules (p.188) have no magnetic moment (↑) of their own. In a magnetic field (↑), diamagnetic materials become weakly magnetized (p.90) in a direction opposite to that of the field.

paramagnetic (*adj*) of a material in which each atom (p.139) or molecule (p.188) has its own magnetic moment (↑), but where they do not line up if there is no outside magnetic field (↑). If there is a magnetic field, the magnetic dipoles (↑) will line up, so the material becomes weakly magnetized (p.90) in the same direction as the field.

ferromagnetic (*adj*) of a solid where each atom (p.139) or molecule (p.188) has its own magnetic moment (↑), and where the forces between them are strong enough to form domains (p.91) where all the magnetic moments point in the same direction. Each domain will be strongly magnetized (p.90), even when there is no outside magnetic field (↑). If most of the domains are magnetized in the same direction, the material will be a permanent magnet (p.91). The only elements (p.139) which are ferromagnetic at room temperature are iron, nickel and cobalt.

Barkhausen effect a coil (p.115) of wire around a ferromagnetic (p.93) core (p.240) will produce an e.m.f. (p.105) when the direction of the domains (p.91) in the core is changed by bringing a permanent magnet (p.91) close to the core. The effect of this can be heard as a rushing sound by using an amplifier (p.242) and loudspeaker (p.58) connected to the coil.

susceptibility (*n*) a measure of how much a magnetic field (p.92) has been increased by a magnetic (p.90) material. $\chi = \mu_r - 1$, where χ is the susceptibility and μ_r is the relative permeability (↓).

permeability (*n*) relative permeability (↓) multiplied by the permeability of free space (p.114).

relative permeability the number of times a magnetic field (p.92) is increased by a magnetic (p.90) material, compared to what it would be in a vacuum (p.242).

hysteresis (*n*) the fact that the magnetization (p.90) of a ferromagnetic (p.93) material depends not only on its magnetic field (p.92) at a particular time, but also on its magnetic (p.90) history.

hysteresis loop a series of lines on a graph showing how magnetization (p.90) varies with magnetic field (p.92), for the magnetic field getting larger and getting smaller.

saturation[1] (*n*) the state of a ferromagnetic (p.93) material when all its domains (p.91) are pointing in the same direction. It is then fully magnetized (p.90) and therefore cannot be magnetized any further.

remnance (*n*) the amount of magnetization (p.90) which remains in a ferromagnetic (p.93) material when the outside magnetic field (p.92) is zero. Permanent magnets (p.91) are made from materials with high remnance.

coercive force the strength of magnetic field (p.92) needed for the demagnetization (p.91) of a ferromagnetic (p.93) material which has been fully magnetized (p.90). Transformer (p.123) cores (p.240) are made from materials with a low coercive force in order to reduce energy losses.

Barkhausen effect

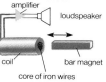

amplifier
loudspeaker
coil
bar magnet
core of iron wires

hysteresis

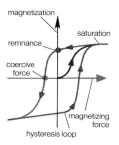

magnetization
saturation
remnance
coercive force
magnetizing force
hysteresis loop

electrostatic (*adj*) concerned with charges (↓) which are not moving. **electrostatics** (*n*).

static electricity the common name for the cause of electrostatic (↑) effects.

charge (*n*) the quality an object must have if it is to have any electrostatic (↑) effect. Two charges of the same type will repel (p.239) one another; two charges of the opposite type will attract (p.239). An electric current (p.103) is a moving charge. **charged** (*adj*), **charge** (*v*).

positive (*adj*) having one of the two types of charge (↑), opposite of negative.

negative (*adj*) having one of the two types of charge (↑), opposite of positive.

coulomb (*n*) the SI unit (p.8) of charge (↑). If a wire carries a current (p.103) of one amp (p.103), a charge of one coulomb passes any point in that wire every second. **C** (*abbr*).

charge on an electron the charge (↑) carried by an electron (p.139) is negative, and a universal constant (p.234). $e = 1.602 \times 10^{-19}$ C, where e is the charge on an electron.

neutral (*adj*) having no charge (↑), or an equal amount of positive and negative charge. Since atoms (p.139) contain both positive and negative charges, objects made of atoms can be neutral only in the second sense. **neutralize** (*v*).

charging by friction the charging (↑) of two neutral (↑) objects by rubbing them together. The friction (p.15) between them may cause some electrons (p.139) to move from one to the other. The object that gains electrons will now have a negative charge, and the object that loses electrons will have an equal positive charge. The direction in which the charge moves depends on the arrangement of electrons in the atoms (p.139) or molecules (p.188) of the two materials.

charging by friction

uncharged
cloth

uncharged
polythene
rod   1

rod rubbed
with cloth

2

rod and cloth
have equal
and opposite
charges

3

induced charge a charge (p.95) produced by
moving the charges in an object which was
neutral (p.95) because it had equal amounts of
positive and negative charge. These charges will
be separated if they are free to move and
another charge is nearby. The electrons (p.139)
in the object will be pushed away from the
nearby charge if it is negative, and pulled
towards it if it is positive. Thus one end of the
object will become negative and the other
positive, but the amounts of each charge will still
be equal.

charging by induction the method of charging
(p.95) an object by giving it an induced charge
(↑). When a charge has been induced, a
connection (p.104) to earth is made. Electrons
(p.139) then move to or from earth (↓),
depending on the sign of the charge causing the
induced charge. The earth connection is then
taken away, leaving the object charged.

electric dipole a pair of equal charges (p.95), one
positive, one negative. At distances which are
large compared to the distance between the two
charges, the electric field (↓) of an electric dipole
is inversely proportional (p.235) to the third
power of the distance from the dipole.

conductor (n) a material in which charges (p.95)
can move so that an electric current (p.103) can
flow. In metals current is carried by electrons
(p.139). Some other materials allow ions (p.139)
to move, e.g. ionic solutions (p.237), molten
ionically bonded (p.221) compounds (p.236) and
ionized gases. **conduct** (v).

induced charge

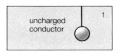

charging by induction

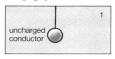

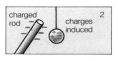

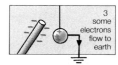

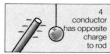

conductor

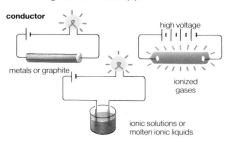

high voltage

metals or graphite

ionized
gases

ionic solutions or
molten ionic liquids

electric dipole

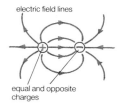

electric field lines

equal and opposite
charges

**law of conservation
of charge**

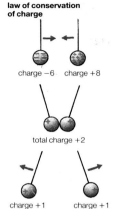

charge −6   charge +8

total charge +2

charge +1   charge +1

electric field

electric field = $\dfrac{F}{q}$

small charge q force F

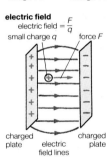

charged   electric   charged
plate   field lines plate

gold leaf electroscope

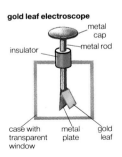

metal cap
metal rod
insulator
case with   metal   gold
transparent plate   leaf
window

insulators

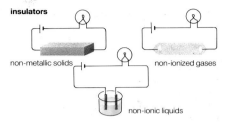

non-metallic solids   non-ionized gases

non-ionic liquids

insulator (*n*) a material in which charges (p.95) cannot move, with the result that no electric current (p.103) can flow. **insulate** (*v*), **insulation** (*n*).

earth (*v*) to connect (p.104) to the earth, or to anything from which there is a conducting (↑) path to the earth. Also known as **ground**.

ground (*v*) = earth (↑).

law of conservation of charge charge (p.95) cannot appear or disappear, but can only move from one place to another.

electric field the effects of electrostatic (p.95) charges (p.95) are explained by saying that every charge produces an electric field in the space around it. The strength of this field at a point is a measure of the effect there will be on any other charges placed at this point. A charge placed at a point where the electric field is one volt per metre will feel a force of one newton (p.14) for every coulomb (p.95) of its charge, if the charge is not large enough to change the arrangement of charges causing the electric field. SI unit (p.8): volt per metre ($V\,m^{-1}$).

electric field lines lines drawn to show the direction of the force on a positive charge (p.95) at any point in an electric field (↑). The closer together these lines are, the stronger the electric field.

electroscope (*n*) an instrument for detecting electric charges (p.95) or measuring their electric potential (p.98).

gold leaf electroscope an electroscope (↑) which works by using charge (p.95) to push a thin sheet of gold away from a metal plate.

Coulomb's law

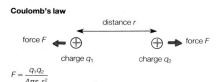

$$F = \frac{q_1 q_2}{4\pi\varepsilon_0 r^2}$$

Coulomb's law the force between two charges
(p.95) is equal to $q_1 q_2/4\pi\varepsilon_0 r^2$, where q_1 and
q_2 are the two charges, r is the distance
between them, and ε_0 is the permittivity of free
space ($\downarrow$).

permittivity of free space a universal constant
(p.234). $\varepsilon_0 = 8.854 \times 10^{-12}\mathrm{Fm^{-1}}$, where ε_0 is
the permittivity of free space.

electric potential a measure of the work (p.17)
needed to put a charge (p.95) in place in an
electric field (p.97). The electric potential at a
point is the amount of work needed to bring a
small charge from infinity to that point, divided
by the size of the charge. SI unit (p.8): volt
(p.107).

electric potential

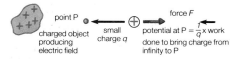

equipotential lines lines joining points which are
all at the same electric potential ($\uparrow$).
Equipotential lines are always at 90° to electric
field lines (p.97).

equipotential lines

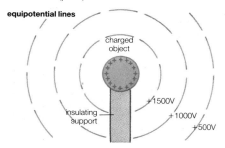

electric field around a conductor

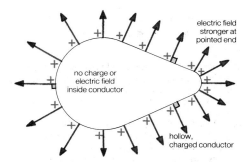

electric field stronger at pointed end

no charge or electric field inside conductor

hollow, charged conductor

electric field around a conductor if a conductor (p.96) is charged (p.95), the forces between the charges in it will cause those charges to move so that: (i) there will be no charge or electric field (p.97) on the inside of a hollow conductor; (ii) the whole of the conductor will be at the same electric potential (↑); (iii) the electric field will be at 90° to the surface of the conductor; and (iv) the charges will be closest together, and the electric field strongest, where the conductor is most curved.

ionization at a point if a pointed object is given a charge (p.95), the electric field (p.97) at the point may be so strong that the force on the nearby air molecules (p.188) is enough to ionize (p.139) them. The ions with the same sign of charge as the charge on the point are then pushed away from the point, so a charged point can be used to make a stream of ions.

ionization at a point

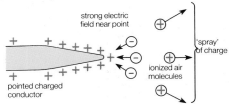

strong electric field near point

'spray' of charge

ionized air molecules

pointed charged conductor

Gauss' law

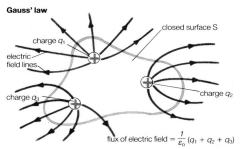

$$\text{flux of electric field} = \frac{1}{\varepsilon_0}(q_1 + q_2 + q_3)$$

Gauss' law the flux (p.241) of electric field (p.97) through any closed surface is equal to the charge (p.95) inside that surface divided by the permittivity of free space (p.98).

van de Graaff generator a machine for making a large electrostatic (p.95) charge (p.95). Charge is forced onto a moving insulator (p.97) by ionization at a point (p.99). The charge is then carried to an area of high electric potential (p.98), where ionization at a point carries the charge onto a large conductor (p.96), where the charge becomes gradually larger and larger.

spark (*n*) an area of strong ionization (p.139) caused by an electric field (p.97) which is large enough to pull electrons (p.139) away from their atoms (p.139). Light and sound are produced from the energy released.

lightning (*n*) a large spark (↑) caused by the gradual increase in charge (p.95) in thunderclouds. The sound of this spark is heard as thunder.

lightning conductor a conductor (p.96), with a point at one end, and a thick earth (p.97) connection (p.104) at the other. It is placed at the top of tall buildings to stop damage by lightning (↑). The charge (p.95) in thunderclouds produces an induced charge (p.96) in the lightning conductor, which sends a stream of ions (p.139) into the cloud because of ionization at a point (p.99). This neutralizes (p.95) the charge in the cloud. If lightning does hit the building, the lightning conductor also acts as a low resistance (p.108) path to earth for the current (p.103).

van de Graaff generator

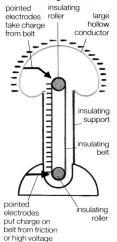

pointed electrodes insulating roller large hollow conductor / take charge from belt / insulating support / insulating belt / pointed electrodes put charge on belt from friction or high voltage / insulating roller

lightning conductor

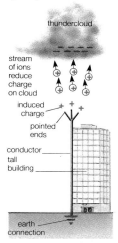

thundercloud / stream of ions reduce charge on cloud / induced charge / pointed ends / conductor / tall building / earth connection

capacitor (*n*) a store of charge (p.95) which is made from two conductors (p.96) separated by a vacuum (p.242) or an insulator (p.97). The conductors are often thin metal sheets, called *plates*. The plates are given opposite charges. The capacitor is also a store of electrical potential energy (p.18).

condenser[2] (*n*) an old name for capacitor (↑).

capacitance (*n*) the measure of the ability of a capacitor (↑) to store charge (p.95). $C = Q/V$, where C is the capacitance, Q the charge on the capacitor, and V the potential difference (p.107) between the plates of the capacitor.

farad (*n*) the SI unit (p.8) of capacitance (↑). A capacitor (↑) has a capacitance of one farad if there is a potential difference (p.107) across it of one volt (p.107) when it stores a charge (p.95) of one coulomb (p.95). **F** (*abbr*).

dielectric (*n*) any insulating (p.97) material which is placed in an electric field (p.97), especially in a capacitor (↑). This material increases the capacitance (↑) of the capacitor (*see polarization* (↓)).

dielectric constant the number of times that the capacitance (↑) of a capacitor (↑) is increased by using a dielectric (↑) between the plates, rather than a vacuum (p.242). Also known as **relative permittivity**.

permittivity (*n*) relative permittivity (↓) multiplied by the permittivity of free space (p.98).

relative permittivity = dielectric constant (↑).

polarization (*n*) the lining up of polar molecules (p.102) in an electric field (p.97) so that they all tend to point in the same direction. In a capacitor (↑) this causes induced charges (p.96) on the surface of the dielectric (↑), which reduce the electric field in the dielectric and so increase the capacitance (↑).

polarization

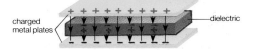

charged metal plates — dielectric

polar molecule a molecule (p.188) in which charge (p.95) is not arranged symmetrically (p.232), e.g. water, hydrogen chloride. The molecule can be thought of as having a small positive charge at one end, and an equal negative charge at the other.

polar molecule

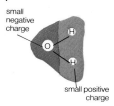

small negative charge

small positive charge

parallel plate capacitor

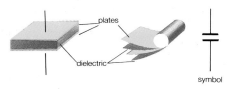

plates

dielectric

symbol

parallel plate capacitor the simplest form of capacitor (p.101). Two parallel conducting (p.96) plates separated by a dielectric (p.101). The capacitance (p.101) is $\varepsilon A/d$, where ε is the permittivity (p.101) of the dielectric, A the area of the plates, and d the distance between them.

capacitors in series and parallel

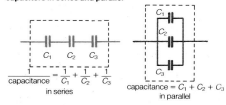

C_1 C_2 C_3

$$\frac{1}{\text{capacitance}} = \frac{1}{C_1} + \frac{1}{C_2} + \frac{1}{C_3}$$
in series

C_1
C_2
C_3

capacitance $= C_1 + C_2 + C_3$
in parallel

capacitors in series and parallel if several capacitors (p.101) of capacitances (p.101) C_1, C_2, C_3, etc. are connected in series (p.106), the capacitance C will be given by
$1/C = 1/C_1 + 1/C_2 + 1/C_3 + ...$
If they are connected in parallel (p.106), then
$C = C_1 + C_2 + C_3 + ...$
energy stored in a capacitor if the energy stored in a capacitor (p.101) is E, then
$E = \frac{1}{2}CV^2 = \frac{1}{2}Q^2/C = \frac{1}{2}QV$, where C is the capacitance (p.101), Q is the charge (p.95) on the capacitor, and V is the potential difference (p.107) across the capacitor.

amp

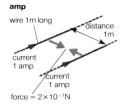

wire 1m long

distance 1m

current 1 amp

current 1 amp

force = 2×10^{-7}N

ammeter

moving coil ammeter

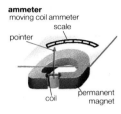

scale

pointer

coil

permanent magnet

moving iron ammeter

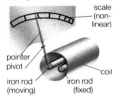

scale (non-linear)

pointer
pivot

coil

iron rod (moving)

iron rod (fixed)

hot wire ammeter

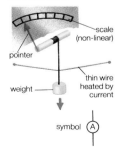

scale (non-linear)

pointer

weight

thin wire heated by current

symbol ⒜

current (n) the flow of charge (p.95); the amount of charge passing a point in one second. In metals the current is carried by electrons (p.139). In ionic solutions (p.237), molten ionically bonded (p.221) compounds (p.236) and ionized (p.139) gases, the charge is carried by ions (p.139).

amp (n) the SI unit (p.8) of current (↑). Two parallel wires, one metre apart in a vacuum (p.242), each carrying a current of one amp, will have a force between them of 2×10^{-7} newton (p.14) on each metre of their length. **A** (abbr). Also known as **ampere**.

ampere (n) = amp (↑).

conventional current the flow of current (↑) around a circuit (p.104). It is thought of as being from the positive terminal (p.104) of a battery (p.104) around the circuit to the negative terminal, even though the charge (p.95) carriers may be moving the other way.

electron current the flow of electrons (p.139), taken as being in the direction the electrons are actually moving, i.e. from the negative terminal (p.104) of a battery (p.104) around the circuit to the positive terminal. This is the opposite direction to conventional current (↑).

drift velocity the average velocity (p.10) with which charge (p.95) carriers are moving. The actual speed of any charge carrier will usually be much more than this, but it is the small difference in the number of charge carriers moving in different directions that causes an electric current (↑).

ammeter (n) an instrument for measuring current (↑). It should have a low resistance (p.108) so as not to change the current flowing through it.

moving coil ammeter an ammeter (↑) which works by measuring the couple on a coil in a magnetic field (p.117).

moving iron ammeter an ammeter (↑) which uses the magnetic field (p.92) produced by the current (↑) to produce a force on a piece of iron, or magnetize (p.90) two pieces of iron so that one is pushed further from the other.

hot wire ammeter an ammeter (↑) which works by measuring the change in length of a piece of wire caused by the current's heating effect (↑).

circuit (*n*) a continuous conducting (p.96) path from one terminal (↓) of a battery (or other power supply) to the other.

short circuit a circuit (↑) of unusually low resistance (p.108). This is usually caused by some fault or incorrect connection (↓), and may cause a danger of fire due to the heat produced by the large current (p.103) that may flow.

open circuit a circuit (↑) that has a break in it, so no current (p.103) can flow.

connection, connexion (*n*) a join between two conductors (p.96), to make a conducting (p.96) path between them. **connect** (*v*).

contact (*n*) a connection (↑), particularly one that is made to be moved or broken, e.g. in a switch (↓).

terminal (*n*) a conductor (p.96) by which something is connected (↑) into a circuit (↑).

switch (*n*) a means of completing or breaking a circuit (↑).

cell (*n*) a producer of electromotive force (↓), turning chemical energy (p.17) into electrical energy (p.111). It is made from two electrodes (p.113) and an electrolyte (p.113). One electrode gains a positive charge (p.95) and the other a negative charge.

switches

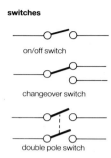

on/off switch

changeover switch

double pole switch

cell

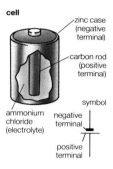

zinc case (negative terminal)

carbon rod (positive terminal)

symbol

ammonium chloride (electrolyte)

negative terminal

positive terminal

battery

cells connected in series

symbols

battery (*n*) a number of cells (↑) connected (↑) together. They are usually connected in series (p.106) to produce a larger electromotive force (↓).

rechargeable battery a battery (↑) where the chemical reactions (p.236) are reversible (p.207), so that it can also turn electrical energy (p.111) into chemical energy (p.17).

recharge (v) to force current (p.103) through a rechargeable battery (↑), changing electrical energy (p.111) into chemical energy (p.17).

standard cell a cell (↑) whose e.m.f. (↓) is known exactly, and which does not change with time, though it may change with temperature (p.181). Standard cells often have a high internal resistance (p.109), and so cannot be used to drive currents (p.103) around circuits (↑). They are used to calibrate (p.240) voltage (p.107) measuring instruments or potentiometer circuits (p.112).

electromotive force the potential difference (p.107) between the terminals (↑) of a supply of electrical energy (p.111) when it is not supplying any current (p.103); the amount of energy that is turned into electrical energy for each coulomb (p.95) of charge (p.95). SI unit (p.8): volt (p.107). **e.m.f.** (abbr).

thermoelectric effect

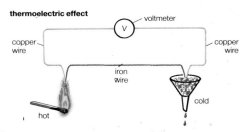

thermoelectric effect when two wires made of different metals join at two points which are at different temperatures (p.181), they cause a current (p.103) to flow. The current depends on the difference in temperature between the points.

thermoelectric e.m.f. the electromotive force (↑) that causes the current (p.103) in the thermoelectric effect (↑).

thermocouple (n) a pair of wires made from different metals connected (↑) together for the purpose of using the thermoelectric effect (↑), particularly for measuring temperatures (p.181).

thermopile (*n*) several thermocouples (p.105) connected (p.104) in series (↓) to produce a larger thermoelectric e.m.f. (p.105), e.g. for measuring infra-red (p.88) radiation (p.241).

piezo-electric (*adj*) of a material which produces an electromotive force (p.105) when force is applied.

photovoltaic cell a producer of electromotive force (p.105) which works by turning light energy into electrical energy (p.111).

solar cell a photovoltaic cell (↑) which uses sunlight to power electrical machines.

solar panel a battery (p.104) of solar cells (↑) on a flat surface, usually placed to receive as much sunlight as possible. They are used to make electrical power for space vehicles, etc.

in series of objects connected (p.104) so that current (p.103) must flow through first one then another.

photovoltaic cell

thin layer of
gold (transparent)

copper oxide

copper

light

current

A

ammeter

symbol

in series

in parallel

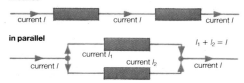

in parallel of objects connected (p.104) so the current (p.103) can flow through either one or the other.

law of conservation of current current (p.103) cannot appear from nowhere and cannot be destroyed. If several wires are connected (p.104) together at a point, the current flowing into the connection must be equal to the current flowing away from it.

law of conservation of current

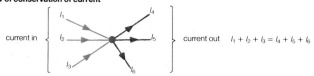

Kirchhoff's laws

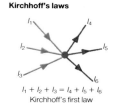

$I_1 + I_2 + I_3 = I_4 + I_5 + I_6$
Kirchhoff's first law

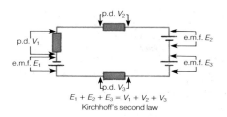

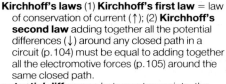

$E_1 + E_2 + E_3 = V_1 + V_2 + V_3$
Kirchhoff's second law

voltmeter

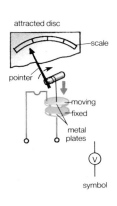

Kirchhoff's laws (1) **Kirchhoff's first law** = law of conservation of current (↑); (2) **Kirchhoff's second law** adding together all the potential differences (↓) around any closed path in a circuit (p.104) must be equal to adding together all the electromotive forces (p.105) around the same closed path.

potential difference between two points, the amount of electrical energy (p.111) which is turned into other forms of energy for every coulomb (p.95) of charge (p.95) passing between those points. SI unit (p.8): volt (↓). **p.d.** (*abbr*).

volt (*n*) the SI unit (p.8) of electromotive force (p.105) and potential difference (↑). The potential difference between two points is one volt if one joule (p.17) of electrical energy (p.111) is turned into other forms of energy for every coulomb (p.95) of charge (p.95) that flows between the two points. **V** (*abbr*).

voltage (*n*) either electromotive force (p.105) or potential difference (↑); the number of volts (↑).

voltmeter (*n*) an instrument for measuring voltage (↑). It should have a very high resistance (p.108) so that the current (p.103) in the circuit (p.104) being examined is not changed.

moving coil voltmeter a voltmeter (↑) using a galvanometer (p.117) to measure the current (p.103) through a high resistance (p.108).

digital voltmeter a voltmeter (↑) using electronics (p.139) to produce a reading of voltage (↑) directly as a series of numbers, rather than using a pointer.

electrometer (*n*) a voltmeter (↑) with a very high resistance (p.108).

resistance (*n*) a measure of how large a potential difference (p.107) is needed to produce a certain current (p.103). Resistance equals potential difference divided by current.

ohm (*n*) the SI unit (p.8) of resistance (↑). If a potential difference (p.107) of one volt (p.107) is needed to make a current (p.103) of one amp (p.103) flow, then the resistance is one ohm. Ω (*abbr*).

Ohm's law for a metal at fixed temperature (p.181) and pressure (p.30), the current (p.103) that flows will be proportional (p.235) to the potential difference (p.107). Ohm's law is also true for some non-metals.

ohmic (*adj*) of a material which obeys Ohm's law (↑).

resistor (*n*) part of a circuit (p.104) made to have a particular resistance (↑).

variable resistor a resistor (↑) whose resistance (↑) can be changed by moving a contact along a length of resistance wire (↓) or similar material.

resistance wire a metal alloy (p.236) wire which is made to have a certain resistance (↑) per metre of length.

potential divider two resistors (↑) connected (p.104) so that when a potential difference (p.107) is connected across both of them, a certain part of that potential difference appears across one of the resistors. If the resistors are R_1 and R_2, and the potential difference across the pair is V, the potential difference across R_2 will be $V \times R_2/(R_1 + R_2)$.

resistance

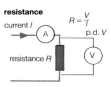

$$R = \frac{V}{I}$$

Ohm's law

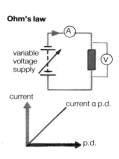

resistor

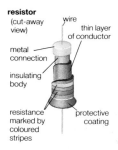

potential divider

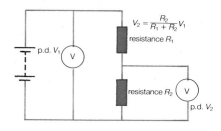

$$V_2 = \frac{R_2}{R_1 + R_2} V_1$$

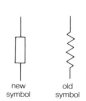

new symbol   old symbol

rheostat (*n*) a variable resistor (↑), particularly a low resistance (↑) type with only two of the three connections (p.104) used.

potentiometer (*n*) (1) a variable resistor (↑), particularly one with all three connections (p.104) used, so that the variable resistor is used as a potential divider (↑); (2) sometimes used as the name for a fixed potential divider (↑) (*see also potentiometer circuit* (p.112)).

resistance box a box containing several resistors (↑), any of which can be connected (p.104) in series (p.106) so as to make any resistance (↑) desired.

internal resistance

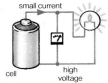

small current

cell high voltage

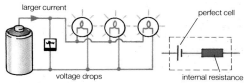

larger current

voltage drops

perfect cell

internal resistance

internal resistance a measure of the fact that a cell (p.104) or other producer of electromotive force (p.105) cannot provide an infinitely large current (p.103), as a perfect cell would be able to. A real cell is thought of as being a perfect cell in series (p.106) with an internal resistance, the value of which can be measured from the fall in potential difference (p.107) across the terminals (p.104) of the cell when a current flows.

resistors in series and parallel if several resistances (↑) R_1, R_2, R_3, etc. are connected in series (p.106), the resistance is R, where $R = R_1 + R_2 + R_3 + ...$ If they are in parallel (p.106), $1/R = 1/R_1 + 1/R_2 + 1/R_3 + ...$

resistors in series and parallel

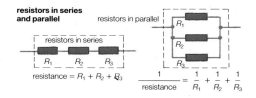

resistors in parallel

resistors in series

R_1 R_2 R_3

resistance = $R_1 + R_2 + R_3$

R_1

R_2

R_3

$$\frac{1}{\text{resistance}} = \frac{1}{R_1} + \frac{1}{R_2} + \frac{1}{R_3}$$

shunt

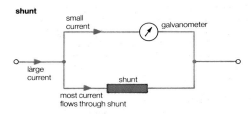

multiplier

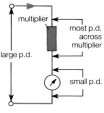

shunt (*n*) a resistor (p.108) connected (p.104) in parallel (p.106) with a galvanometer (p.117) to allow it to measure higher currents (p.103).

multiplier (*n*) a resistor (p.108) connected (p.104) in series (p.106) with a galvanometer (p.117) to allow it to be used to measure voltages (p.107).

heating effect of a current when a current (p.103) flows, the moving charge (p.95) carriers hit the atoms (p.139) of the conductor (p.96). This makes the atoms vibrate (p.242) more quickly, so that the conductor becomes warmer. The rate at which heat energy (p.18) is put into the conductor is equal to the potential difference (p.107) between the ends of the conductor multiplied by the current through it.

fuse[1] (*n*) a thin piece of wire which has a low melting point (p.192). If too much current (p.103) flows through the fuse, the wire gets hot and then melts. This stops the current, and prevents any damage that might have been caused by too much current flowing in the rest of the circuit (p.104).

resistivity (*n*) a measure of the resistance (p.108) of a material which depends only on the material and not on how long or how thick the piece of material is. $R = \rho l / A$, where R is the resistance of the piece of material, ρ is its resistivity, A is its area of cross section (p.233), and l is its length. SI unit (p.8): ohm (p.108) metre (Ωm).

temperature coefficient of resistance a measure of how resistance (p.108) changes with changes in temperature (p.181).
$R = R_0 (1 + a\theta)$, where R is the resistance at temperature θ°C, R_0 is the resistance at 0°C, and a is the temperature coefficient of resistance.

fuse

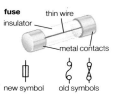

resistivity

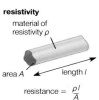

resistance $= \dfrac{\rho l}{A}$

temperature coefficient of resistance

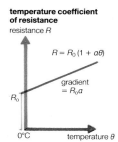

a = temperature coefficient of resistance

thermistor
semiconductor

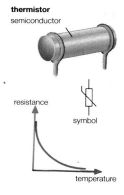

resistance

symbol

temperature

thermistor (*n*) a resistor (p.108) which has a large temperature coefficient of resistance (↑). They are usually made from semiconductors (p.132), which have large negative temperature coefficients of resistance, so the resistance (p.108) gets lower at high temperatures (p.181).

conductivity (*n*) the reciprocal of resistivity (↑). SI unit (p.8): siemens (↓) per metre (S m⁻¹).

electrical energy energy possessed by charge (p.95) carriers which are at a higher electric potential (p.98) than they would be if they were at another point in the circuit. If a current (p.103) flows between two points which have a potential difference (p.107) between them of *V*, the amount of electrical energy turned into other types of energy is equal to *V* multiplied by the amount of charge flowing between the points. If the current flowing is *I*, and it flows for a time *t*, the energy is *IVt*.

electrical power the amount of electrical energy (↑) turned into other types of energy each second. If the potential difference (p.107) between two points in a circuit (p.104) is *V*, and the current (p.103) is *I*, the power is *IV*. If the resistance (p.108) of this part of the circuit is *R*, the power is also I^2R or V^2/R.

maximum power theorem the electrical power (↑) supplied to a load (p.239) resistance (p.108) by a battery (p.104) or other producer of e.m.f. (p.105) is largest when the resistance of the load is equal to the internal resistance (p.109) of the supply.

maximum power theorem

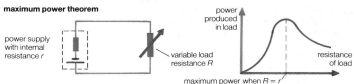

power supply
with internal
resistance *r*

variable load
resistance *R*

power produced in load

resistance of load

maximum power when *R* = *r*

conductance (*n*) the reciprocal of resistance (p.108).

siemens (*n*) the SI unit (p.8) of conductance (↑). A resistance (p.108) of one ohm (p.108) has a conductance of one siemens. **S** (*abbr*).

potentiometer circuit a circuit (p.104) which uses a potentiometer (p.109) to compare an unknown potential difference (p.107) with a known one. The method does not take any current (p.103) from the circuit where the potential difference is measured, so a potentiometer circuit behaves like a perfect voltmeter (p.107), i.e. one through which no current flows. The circuit must first be calibrated (p.240) using a standard cell (p.105), and can only measure potential differences which are less than that provided by the cell which supplies the current to the potentiometer itself. A simple form of potentiometer circuit uses a metre length of resistance wire (p.108), with a sliding contact (p.104) as the potentiometer (*see metre bridge* (↓)).

driver cell a cell (p.104) which is used to supply current (p.103) to a potentiometer circuit (↑).

Wheatstone bridge a potentiometer circuit (↑) in which the driver cell (↑) also supplies a current (p.103) to a potential divider (p.108) with one known resistance (p.108) and one unknown resistance. In this way it is possible to measure the value of the unknown resistance. With an a.c. (p.125) supply, the Wheatstone bridge can also be used to measure impedances (p.129).

potentiometer circuit

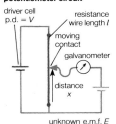

when galvanometer reads
zero, $E = \frac{x}{l} V$

Wheatstone bridge

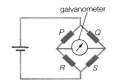

when galvanometer reads
zero, $\frac{P}{Q} = \frac{R}{S}$

metre bridge

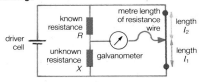

when galvanometer reads
zero, $X = \frac{l_1}{l_2} R$

metre bridge a Wheatstone bridge (↑) in which the potentiometer (p.109) is a metre length of resistance wire (p.108) with a sliding contact (p.104). With this, the resistances (p.108) in the two parts of a circuit (p.104) can be compared directly by measuring the length of the wire in each part. Also known as **slide-wire bridge**.

slide-wire bridge = metre bridge (↑).

electrolysis

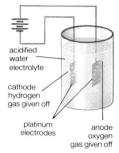

acidified
water
electrolyte

cathode
hydrogen
gas given off

platinum
electrodes

anode
oxygen
gas given off

electroplating

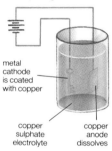

metal
cathode
is coated
with copper

copper
sulphate
electrolyte

copper
anode
dissolves

electrolysis (*n*) the flow of current (p.103) through a liquid, causing chemical (p.236) changes. Electrolysis is an important method of obtaining pure samples of reactive (p.236) metals.

electrolyte (*n*) the liquid through which current (p.103) flows in electrolysis (↑) or in a cell (p.104).

electrode (*n*) the connection (p.104) between a solid conductor (p.96), usually a metal, and a liquid, gas or vacuum (p.242).

anode (*n*) an electrode (↑) with a positive charge (p.95).

anion (*n*) an ion (p.139) with a negative charge (p.95), i.e. one which feels a force towards an anode (↑).

cathode (*n*) an electrode (↑) with a negative charge (p.95).

cation (*n*) an ion (p.139) with a positive charge (p.95), i.e. one which feels a force towards a cathode (↑).

electroplating (*n*) the electrolysis (↑) of an ionic solution (p.237) containing metal ions (p.139) which form a metal film on the cathode (↑), whilst the anode (↑), which is made of the metal concerned, dissolves (p.237) to replace the metal ions lost from the solution.

Faraday's law of electrolysis the mass of material that appears from an ionic solution (p.237), or disappears into an ionic solution, at an electrode (↑), is proportional (p.235) to the amount of charge (p.95) flowing through the electrolyte (↑). Also, for a given amount of charge, the mass of material is directly proportional to the relative atomic mass (p.155) of the ions (p.139) concerned, divided by their charge.

faraday (*n*) the amount of charge (p.95) carried by one mole (p.237) of ions (p.139), each of which has a positive or negative charge equal in size to the charge on an electron (p.139). One faraday equals 96 487 coulomb (p.95). Not to be confused with farad (p.101), which is a unit (p.8) of capacitance (p.101). Also known as **Faraday constant**.

Faraday constant = faraday (↑).

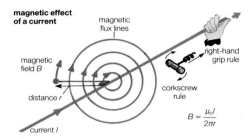

magnetic effect of a current
magnetic flux lines
magnetic field B
right-hand grip rule
distance r
corkscrew rule
current I

$$B = \frac{\mu_0 I}{2\pi r}$$

magnetic effect of a current when a current
(p.103) flows in a wire, it produces a magnetic
field (p.92). The magnetic flux lines (p.92) around
a long straight wire are circles in a plane (p.233)
at 90° to the direction of the wire. If the current is
I, the magnetic field at a distance r from the wire
is $\mu_0 I/2\pi r$, where μ_0 is the permeability of free
space ($\downarrow$).

permeability of free space a constant (p.234), the
value of which results from the definition (p.238) of
the amp (p.103). $\mu_0 = 4\pi \times 10^{-7}\,\mathrm{H\,m^{-1}}$,
where μ_0 is the permeability of free space.

corkscrew rule the direction of the magnetic flux
lines (p.92) around a straight wire carrying a
current (p.103) is the same as the direction a
right-handed screw would have to be turned to
move it along the wire in the same direction as
the conventional current (p.103) in the wire.

right-hand grip rule the direction of the magnetic
flux lines (p.92) around a wire carrying a current
(p.103) is the same as the direction of the fingers
of a right hand point when the wire is held with
the thumb pointing in the direction of the
conventional current (p.103) in the wire.

solenoid (n) a coil ($\downarrow$) of wire which has a length
which is large compared to its diameter. The
magnetic field (p.92) at the centre of a long
solenoid in a vacuum (p.242) is $\mu_0 n I$, where μ_0 is
the permeability of free space ($\uparrow$), n is the
number of turns of wire in each metre length of
the solenoid, and I is the current (p.103) in the
solenoid. The field at each end of the solenoid is
half the field at the centre.

solenoid

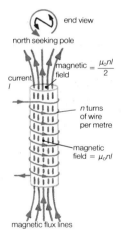

end view
north seeking pole

current I

$$\text{magnetic field} = \frac{\mu_0 n I}{2}$$

n turns of wire per metre

magnetic field $= \mu_0 n I$

magnetic flux lines

end view
south seeking pole

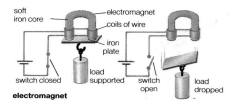

electromagnet

electromagnet (*n*) a solenoid (↑), usually with an
iron core (p.240). When a current (p.103) flows in
the solenoid, the magnetic field (p.92) makes the
domains (p.91) in the iron line up, so producing a
stronger magnetic field which can be used to
pick up objects containing ferromagnetic (p.93)
materials. When the current stops, the iron loses
its magnetism (p.90) and the objects are free to
fall. **electromagnetism** (*n*).

coil (*n*) several turns of wire, insulated (p.97) from
each other so that current (p.103) flows around
each turn, making a stronger magnetic field
(p.92) than the same current in a single piece of
wire.

Helmholtz coils

separation = radius

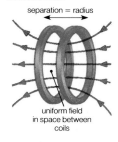
uniform field
in space between
coils

Helmholtz coils a pair of flat coils (↑), the distance
between them being equal to their radius. They
produce a magnetic field (p.92) which changes
very little over the whole of the space between
them.

catapult field the magnetic field (p.92) produced
when a wire in which a current (p.103) is flowing
is placed between the poles (p.90) of a magnet
(p.90). The magnetic field from the wire and the
magnetic field from the magnet together make a
magnetic field which is stronger on one side of
the wire than the other. This causes a force on
the wire in the direction of the area of weaker
field.

catapult field

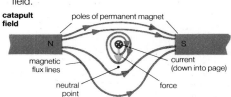

motor effect the force on a current (p.103) carrying wire in a magnetic field (p.92). The force is stronger if the current is larger, if the magnetic field is stronger, or if the wire is made more nearly at 90° to the direction of the magnetic flux lines (p.92).

Fleming's left-hand rule the direction of the force on a current (p.103) carrying wire in a magnetic field (p.92) can be found by holding the thumb, and the first and second fingers of the left hand at 90° to each other. If the first finger points in the direction of the magnetic field and the second finger points in the direction of the conventional current (p.103), then the thumb will be pointing in the direction of the force.

force on a current in a magnetic field if a current (p.103) I flows in a wire of length l in a magnetic field (p.92) B, the force on the wire will be $BIl\sin\alpha$, where α is the angle between the directions of the current and the magnetic field.

force on a charge in a magnetic field if a charge (p.95) q moves with a speed v in a magnetic field (p.92) B, there will be a force on the charge of $Bqv\sin\alpha$, where α is the angle between the direction of motion of the charge and the direction of the magnetic field. This force is the cause of the motor effect (↑) and the e.m.f. (p.105) produced when a wire is moved through a magnetic field.

Biot-Savart law a small part of a wire of length δl carrying a current (p.103) I at a distance r from some point P, causes a small part of the magnetic field (p.92) at P. This small part of the field is δB, where $\delta B = (\mu_0/4\pi)(I\delta l \sin\alpha)/r^2)$, where α is the angle between the piece of wire and the line from this to P, and μ_0 is the permeability of free space (p.114). From this the magnetic field caused by wires of any shape can be found by adding together the effects of each part of the wire.

Fleming's left-hand rule

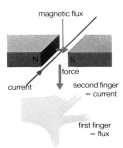

magnetic flux

force

current

second finger = current

first finger = flux

thumb = force

force on a current in a magnetic field

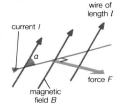

wire of length l

current I

α

force F

magnetic field B

$F = BIl\sin\alpha$

force on a charge in a magnetic field

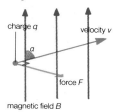

charge q

velocity v

α

force F

magnetic field B

$F = Bqv\sin\alpha$

Biot-Savart law

length δl

α

distance r

magnetic field δB

current I

$$\delta B = \frac{\mu_0}{4\pi}\,\frac{I\delta l\sin\alpha}{r^2}$$

couple on a coil in a magnetic field

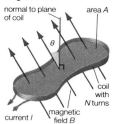

normal to plane of coil

area A

θ

coil with N turns

current I

magnetic field B

couple = $BIAN\sin\theta$

couple on a coil in a magnetic field if a flat coil (p.115) of area A with N turns of wire carrying a current (p.103) I is placed in a magnetic field (p.92) B, there will be a couple (p.26) on the coil equal to $BIAN\sin\theta$, where θ is the angle between the normal (p.234) to the plane (p.233) of the coil and the direction of the magnetic field. This couple does not depend on the shape of the coil, only on its area.

galvanometer (n) an instrument for measuring small currents (p.103).

moving coil galvanometer a galvanometer which operates by measuring the couple on a coil in a magnetic field (↑). This couple (p.26) is opposed by a pair of hairsprings, which also carry the current (p.103) to and from the coil (p.115). The magnetic field (p.92) comes from a permanent magnet (p.91) with curved poles (p.90) and with a fixed piece of soft iron between the poles. This makes a magnetic field which is always in the direction to provide the largest couple on the coil, so the marks on the scale of the galvanometer are evenly spaced. The coil is wound on an aluminium frame, so eddy currents (p.124) damp (p.39) any oscillations (p.35) of the coil.

moving coil galvanometer

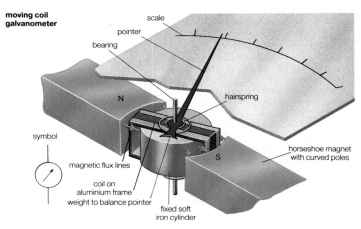

scale

pointer

bearing

N

hairspring

symbol

magnetic flux lines

coil on aluminium frame

weight to balance pointer

S

horseshoe magnet with curved poles

fixed soft iron cylinder

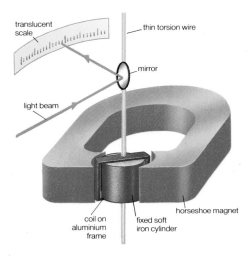

translucent scale

thin torsion wire

mirror

light beam

horseshoe magnet

coil on aluminium frame

fixed soft iron cylinder

torsion wire galvanometer

torsion wire galvanometer a form of moving coil galvanometer (p.117) in which the coil (p.115) is supported not by hairsprings, but by long straight wires. This makes the galvanometer better able to detect small currents (p.103), but also makes it easily damaged by mechanical (p.239) shocks. In these galvanometers the pointer is often a beam of light reflected (p.45) from a small mirror fixed to the coil of the galvanometer.

ballistic galvanometer a galvanometer (p.117) which is made to measure charge (p.95) rather than current (p.103). The charge is passed through the galvanometer as a short burst of current, which sets the coil (p.115) oscillating (p.35). The amplitude (p.36) of these oscillations is proportional (p.235) to the charge. Such a galvanometer must have only slight damping (p.39), so the coil is made on an insulating (p.97) frame to avoid eddy currents (p.124).

Hall effect

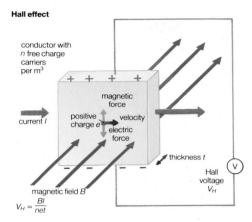

conductor with
n free charge
carriers
per m³

current I

positive
charge e

magnetic
force

velocity

electric
force

thickness t

magnetic field B

Hall
voltage
V_H

$V_H = \dfrac{BI}{net}$

Hall effect when a current (p. 103) flows through a
conductor (p. 96) in a magnetic field (p. 92), the
force on the moving charges (p. 95) causes them
to build up gradually on one side of the conductor
until the resulting electrostatic (p. 95) force is equal
to the magnetic (p. 90) force. Thus there is a
potential difference (p. 107) between the two
sides of the conductor. The Hall effect is much
larger for semiconductors (p. 132) than for metals,
as semiconductors have fewer charge carriers.

Hall voltage the voltage (p. 107) produced in the
Hall effect (↑). It is equal to $BI/(net)$, where B is
the magnetic field (p. 92), I is the current (p. 103),
n is the number of charge (p. 95) carriers in each
metre cubed of the conductor (p. 96), e is the
charge on each charge carrier, and t is the
thickness of the conductor in the direction of the
magnetic field.

Hall coefficient a constant (p. 234) for any given
material, which measures the strength of the Hall
effect (↑) in that material. It is equal to $1/(ne)$,
where n is the number of charge (p. 95) carriers in
each metre cubed of the material, and e is the
charge on each charge carrier.

Hall probe a piece of semiconductor (p. 132) used
to measure magnetic fields (p. 92).

motor

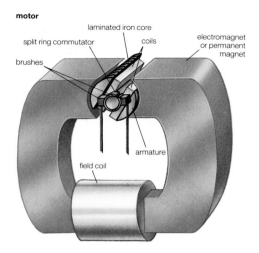

laminated iron core

split ring commutator   coils

electromagnet
or permanent
magnet

brushes

armature

field coil

motor (*n*) a machine which turns when a current
(p.103) flows through it, changing electrical
energy (p.111) into kinetic energy (p.18). It is
made from a coil (p.115) of wire held between
the poles (p.90) of a magnet (p.90), and which is
free to turn. When a current flows, the couple on
the coil in a magnetic field (p.92) makes the coil
turn. To keep it turning for more than half a turn
the direction of the current in the coil must be
changed every half turn. This is done by using a
commutator (↓). In most motors several coils are
used with an iron core (p.240), and the magnet
may be an electromagnet (p.115). Motors made
to operate with alternating current (p.125) have
the magnetic field provided by an electromagnet
so that the magnetic field changes in phase
(p.37) with the changes in current in the armature
(↓).
commutator (*n*) a machine which connects
(p.104) the coils (p.115) in a motor (↑) or dynamo
(p.122) to the opposite terminals (p.104) of the
motor or dynamo each time the coil has turned
through 180°. In this way the motor continues to
turn in the same direction.

split ring commutator a simple commutator (↑) in which each end of each coil (p.115) in a motor (↑) or dynamo (p.122) is connected (p.104) to a piece of a metal ring. Brushes (↓) then carry current (p.103) to and from each section of the ring.

brush (*n*) a contact (p.104) which rubs against the commutator (↑) in a motor (↑) or dynamo (p.122). Brushes are often made of carbon in the form of graphite in order to reduce friction (p.15).

armature (*n*) the moving part of a motor (↑) or dynamo (p.122).

field coil the coil (p.115) of an electromagnet (p.115), used to provide the magnetic field (p.92) for a motor (↑) or dynamo (p.122).

electromagnetic induction

1

bar magnet

coil

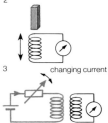

2

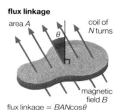

3 changing current

electromagnetic induction when a wire moves or a magnetic field (p.92) changes so that magnetic flux lines (p.92) are cut by the wire, an electromotive force (p.105) will be induced (p.241) in the wire. Thus an electromotive force can be induced in a wire by moving a magnet (p.90) near the wire, by moving the wire near a magnet, or by varying the current (p.103) in an electromagnet (p.115) near the wire.

Faraday's law of electromagnetic induction the electromotive force (p.105) produced in a circuit (p.104) by electromagnetic induction (↑) is equal to the rate of change (p.235) of the flux linkage (↓) in the circuit.

flux linkage the magnetic flux (p.92) through a circuit (p.104) or coil (p.115) multiplied by the number of times the magnetic flux lines (p.92) pass through the circuit. Thus if a coil has *N* turns of wire, the flux linkage through the coil is *N* times the magnetic flux through a single turn of the coil.

flux linkage

area *A*

θ

coil of *N* turns

magnetic field *B*

flux linkage = $BAN\cos\theta$

Lenz's law the direction of an induced (p.241) electromotive force (p.105) is always in the direction to act against the change that caused it. E.g. if a coil (p.115) is moved away from a magnet (p.90), the induced electromotive force will be in such a direction as to try to cause a current (p.103) in the coil which will magnetize (p.90) it in the direction to make it be pulled towards the magnet.

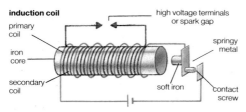

induction coil
primary coil
iron core
secondary coil
high voltage terminals or spark gap
springy metal
soft iron
contact screw

induction coil two coils (p.115) on the same core
(p.240), one having many more turns of wire than
the other. When a current (p.103) flows through
the smaller coil, the core is magnetized (p.90) and
attracts (p.239) a contact (p.104) which breaks
the circuit (p.104). The sudden change in magnetic flux (p.92) produces a very large electromotive force (p.105) across the larger coil. As the
current has stopped flowing, the contact springs
back to connect (p.104) the coil to the power
supply again and these events are repeated.

dynamo (*n*) a machine which turns kinetic energy
(p.18) into electrical energy (p.111). It contains a
coil (p.115) and a magnet (p.90), one of which is
turned to induce (p.241) an electromotive force
(p.105) in the coil. Usually the magnet, which
may be an electromagnet (p.115), is fixed and
the coil turns, the current (p.103) being taken
from the coil through a commutator (p.120), so
the current always flows in the same direction.

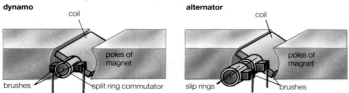

dynamo
coil
poles of magnet
brushes
split ring commutator

alternator
coil
poles of magnet
slip rings
brushes

alternator (*n*) a machine for producing an
alternating current (p.125). It works in the same
way as a dynamo (↑), but the armature (p.121) is
connected (p.104) by a pair of rings, called *slip
rings*, so that the current flows in different
directions at different stages in the motion of the
coil (p.115).

back e.m.f. the electromotive force (p.105) induced (p.241) in a coil (p.115) when the current (p.103) flowing through the coil changes. By Lenz's law (p.121), that electromotive force tries to stop the current from changing, being in the direction to try to keep the current flowing if it is being made less, or to stop it flowing if it is getting larger.

transformer

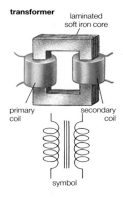

laminated soft iron core

primary coil

secondary coil

symbol

transformer (n) a machine which carries electrical energy (p.111) from one circuit (p.104) to another, using magnetic fields (p.92). It is made of two coils (p.115) on a ferromagnetic (p.93) core (p.240). An alternating current (p.125) in the primary (↓) produces a changing magnetic field which induces (p.241) an electromotive force (p.105) in the secondary (↓). The secondary voltage (p.107) will be equal to the primary voltage multiplied by the turns ratio (↓). The power (p.19) on each side of the transformer is the same, apart from any power that is lost because of heat energy (p.18) produced by the resistance (p.108) of the wires, and by hysteresis (p.94) and eddy currents (p.124) in the core. The core is usually made of a laminated (p.124) material which has a low coercive force (p.94) in order to make these losses of power as small as possible.

primary (n) the coil (p.115) through which energy is fed into a transformer (↑), i.e. the one which is connected (p.104) to a power supply.

secondary (n) the coil (p.115) through which energy is fed out from a transformer (↑), i.e. the one which is connected (p.104) to a load (p.239).

turns ratio the number of turns of wire in the secondary (↑) of a transformer (↑), divided by the number of turns of wire in the primary (↑).

step-up (adj) of a transformer (↑) which has a turns ratio (↑) larger than one. The current (p.103) flowing in the primary (↑) of a step-up transformer will be greater than that in the secondary (↑).

step-down (adj) of a transformer (↑) which has a turns ratio (↑) smaller than one.

eddy current a current (p.103) induced (p.241) in
a large piece of conducting (p.96) material. By
Lenz's law (p.121) this causes forces which
oppose the changes which caused the current.
These currents make the conductor (p.96) hot,
and are usually a waste of energy. The currents
can be made small by making the conductor
laminated (↓). Eddy currents can also be used to
heat conducting materials.

laminated (*adj*) of an object which is made from
layers, particularly sheets of metal separated by
thin layers of insulating (p.97) material. It is used
particularly of the core (p.240) of a transformer
(p.123) or the armature (p.121) of a motor
(p.120) or dynamo (p.122).

search coil a small coil (p.115), usually made with
many turns of thin wire, which is used to
measure magnetic fields (p.92). If the coil is
moved from a place where the flux linkage
(p.121) is ϕ_1 to a place where it is ϕ_2, the charge
(p.95) that flows through the circuit (p.104) will
be $(\phi_1 - \phi_2)/R$, where R is the resistance (p.108)
of the whole circuit. This charge can be
measured using a ballistic galvanometer (p.118).

inductance (*n*) the electromotive force (p.105)
induced (p.241), usually in a coil (p.115), as a
result of a given rate of change (p.235) of a
current (p.103). The electromotive force induced
is equal to the inductance multiplied by the rate
of change of the current.

henry (*n*) the SI unit (p.8) of inductance (↑). The
inductance is one henry if a current (p.103)
changing at the rate of one amp (p.103) per
second induces (p.241) an electromotive force
(p.105) of one volt (p.107). **H** (*abbr*).

self-inductance (*n*) the inductance (↑) which
comes from an electromotive force (p.105)
induced (p.241) in a coil (p.115) because of the
current (p.103) in that coil changing.

mutual inductance the inductance (↑) which
comes from an electromotive force (p.105)
induced (p.241) in a coil (p.115) because of the
current (p.103) changing in another coil nearby.

inductor (*n*) a coil (p.115) made to have a
particular value of self-inductance (↑).

eddy current

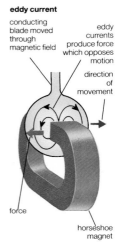

conducting
blade moved
through
magnetic field

eddy
currents
produce force
which opposes
motion

direction
of
movement

force

horseshoe
magnet

search coils

1

2

direct current current (p.103) which always flows in the same direction. Usually used to mean a steady current, e.g. from a cell (p.104), but can also mean bursts of current, all in the same direction, e.g. from a half-wave rectifier (p.131). **d.c.** (*abbr*).

alternating current

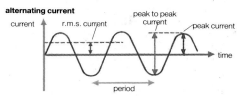

alternating current current (p.103) which flows first in one direction then the other. Usually used to mean a current which oscillates (p.35) sinusoidally (p.234), but can also mean bursts of current flowing in different directions. An **alternating voltage** is a voltage (p.107) which is first in one direction then the other. **a.c.** (*abbr*).

charging a capacitor when a capacitor (p.101) is connected (p.104) to a steady supply of electromotive force (p.105) through a resistor (p.108), it cannot at once charge (p.95) fully, i.e. to the point where the potential difference (p.107) across its plates is equal to the electromotive force of the supply. If the connection is made at time $t = 0$, then at a time t, the potential difference across the capacitor will be $E(1 - \exp(-t/RC))$, where E is the electromotive force of the supply, R is the resistance (p.108), and C is the capacitance (p.101).

charging a capacitor

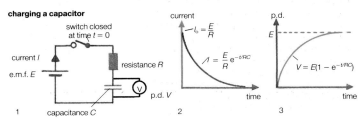

discharging a capacitor

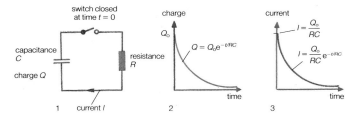

1   2   3

discharging a capacitor if the two plates of a
  charged (p.95) capacitor (p.101) are connected
  (p.104) together through a resistance (p.108) R,
  the capacitor cannot lose all its charge at once,
  as this would produce an infinite current (p.103).
  If the charge at time $t = 0$, when the connection
  is made, is Q_0, then at a later time t, the charge
  will be $Q_0 \exp(-t/RC)$, where C is the
  capacitance (p.101).
time constant the time taken for a current (p.103)
  or voltage (p.107) which is rising or falling in a
  capacitor (p.101) or inductor (p.124) to rise to
  $1/e$ of its finishing value or to fall to $1/e$ of its
  starting value; $e = 2.7183$. For a circuit (p.104)
  with a resistance (p.108) R and capacitance
  (p.101) C, the time constant is RC. With an
  inductance (p.124) L and a resistance R, the time
  constant is L/R.

time constant

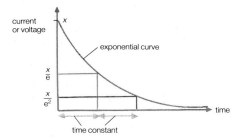

rise and fall of current in an inductor

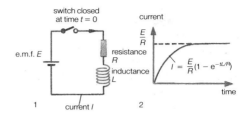

switch closed
at time $t = 0$

current

e.m.f. E

resistance
R

inductance
L

$\frac{E}{R}$

$I = \frac{E}{R}(1 - e^{-tL/R})$

time

1   current I 2

rise and fall of current in an inductor because
of the back e.m.f. (p.105) induced (p.241) in an
inductor (p.124) in which a changing current
(p.103) is flowing, it is not possible for the
current in an inductor to change infinitely
quickly. If at time $t = 0$, an inductor L is
connected (p.104) across a steady supply of
electromotive force (p.105) E, through a
resistance (p.108) R, then at a later time t, the
current will be $(E/R)(1-\exp(-tR/L))$. If the
circuit (p.104) is broken, the current must stop,
so the back e.m.f. will be very large, causing a
spark (p.100).

a.c. power in a resistor if an alternating voltage
(p.125) is connected (p.104) across a resistance
(p.108), the current (p.103) that flows will be in
phase (p.37) with the voltage. The power (p.19),
which appears as heat energy (p.18) in the
resistor (p.108) will be largest when the current
and voltage are largest. The average power for a
sinusoidal (p.234) alternating current (p.125) will
be one half of the largest power.

root mean square the value of alternating
current (p.125) or voltage (p.107) which makes
the power (p.19) in a resistance (p.108) the same
as it would be if a steady current or voltage of the
same value was used. This is found by squaring
the quantity, taking the average of this, and then
calculating the square root of the average. For a
sinusoidal (p.234) voltage or current, the root
mean square value is 0.707 times the largest
value. The voltage of an a.c. supply is usually
given as a root mean square value. **r.m.s.** (*abbr*).

alternating current in a capacitor

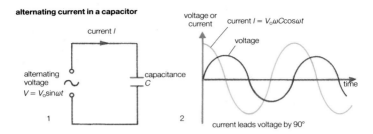

current leads voltage by 90°

alternating current in a capacitor if a sinusoidal
(p.234) alternating voltage (p.125) is placed
across a capacitance (p.101) C, the current
(p.103) that flows will also be sinusoidal, but
there will be a phase difference (p.37) of 90°, with
the current leading the voltage. If the r.m.s.
(p.127) voltage is V, the r.m.s. current will be
$V\omega C$, where ω is the angular frequency (p.37) of
the voltage.

alternating current in an inductor if a sinusoidal
(p.234) alternating voltage (p.125) is placed
across an inductance (p.124) L, the current
(p.103) that flows will also be sinusoidal, but
there will be a phase difference of 90°, with the
voltage leading the current. If the r.m.s. (p.127)
voltage is V, the current will be $V/\omega L$, where ω is
the angular frequency (p.37) of the voltage.

reactance (n) the r.m.s. (p.127) voltage (p.107)
divided by the r.m.s. current (p.103) in a circuit
(p.104) in which a sinusoidal (p.234) alternating
current (p.125) is flowing through a capacitance
(p.101) or an inductance (p.124) without any
resistance (p.108). It is a measure of how easily
the current can flow. For a capacitance C,
$X = 1/\omega C$; for an inductance L, $X = \omega L$, where X
is the reactance, and ω is the angular frequency.
SI unit (p.8): ohm (Ω) (p.108).

CIVIL a way to remember the phase differences
(p.37) between currents (p.103) and voltages
(p.107) in capacitors (p.101) and inductors
(p.124). The order is: current (I) in a capacitor (C);
voltage (V); and current (I) in an inductor (L), each
of these quantities leading the next one by 90°.

**alternating current in
an inductor**

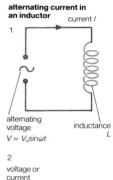

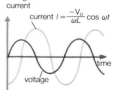

current behind voltage by 90°

phasor

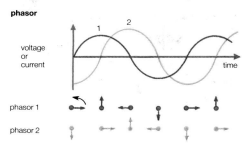

phasor (*n*) a vector (p.10) which shows both the phase (p.37) and size of an alternating current (p.125) or voltage (p.107). Phasors are thought of as turning at a rate equal to the frequency (p.36) of the quantity they represent, and phase differences (p.37) between these quantities are shown by the angle between the phasors. Quantities with different phases can be added together by adding the phasors, using the rules for adding vectors.

impedance (*n*) the r.m.s. (p.127) voltage (p.107) divided by the r.m.s. current (p.103) in a circuit (p.104) which contains both resistance (p.108) and reactance (↑); a measure of how easily current can flow in a circuit. If a circuit contains resistance R, capacitance (p.101) with reactance X_C, and inductance (p.124) with reactance X_L, all in series (p.106), the impedance will be $((R^2 + (X_C - X_L)^2)^{1/2}$. SI unit (p.8): ohm ($\Omega$) (p.108).

power in an a.c. circuit if a sinusoidal (p.234) r.m.s. (p.127) voltage (p.107) V causes an r.m.s. current (p.103) I to flow, with a phase difference (p.37) between voltage and current of θ, the power (p.19) which is lost as heat energy (p.18) is $IV\cos\theta$.

power factor the cosine of the phase difference (p.37) between the current (p.103) and voltage (p.107) in a circuit (p.104) in which an alternating current (p.125) is flowing. If a current flows through a perfect inductor (p.124) or capacitor (p.101), the power factor will be zero, and no heat energy (p.18) will be produced.

inductor and capacitor in series

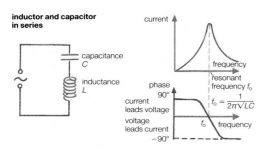

inductor and capacitor in series if an inductor (p.124) and a capacitor (p.101) are in series (p.106), the current (p.103) through each must be the same, so the voltages (p.107) across each will be exactly out of phase (p.37). At the frequency (p.36) at which the inductance (p.124) and capacitance (p.101) have the same reactance (p.128), the voltage across the two together will be zero, so the impedance (p.129) at this frequency will be very small.

inductor and capacitor in parallel if an inductor (p.124) and capacitor (p.101) are in parallel (p.106), the voltage (p.107) across each will be the same, so the currents (p.103) through each will be exactly out of phase (p.37). At the frequency (p.36) at which the reactance (p.128) of the capacitor and the inductor are the same, these currents will be equal and opposite, with the result that the current supplied to the whole circuit (p.104) will be zero, so at this frequency the circuit will have a very high impedance (p.129).

tuned circuit a circuit (p.104) containing an inductor (p.124) and a capacitor (p.101). This circuit will have an impedance (p.129) which is either very large or very small at one particular frequency (p.36), called the *resonant frequency*. If the inductor and capacitor are in series (p.106), the impedance at the resonant frequency is very low. If they are in parallel (p.106), the impedance at the resonant frequency is very high. Also known as **resonant circuit**.

resonant circuit = tuned circuit (↑).

inductor and capacitor in parallel

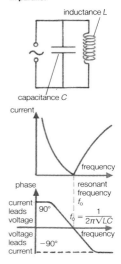

LCR circuit a circuit (p.104) containing inductance (p.124), capacitance (p.101) and resistance (p.108). Any tuned circuit (↑) will always have some resistance as it is not possible to make a coil (p.115) which is a perfect inductance, i.e. one with no resistance. The larger the resistance, the smaller is the change in impedance (p.129) around the resonant frequency (*see tuned circuit* (↑)).

bandwidth (*n*) the difference between the two frequencies (p.36) at which the power (p.19) in a circuit (p.104) falls to one half of its largest value.

rectifier circuit any circuit (p.104) which is used to change an alternating current (p.125) to a direct current (p.125).

half-wave rectifier a rectifier circuit (↑) in which current (p.103) flows during only one half of the oscillation (p.35) of the alternating current (p.125).

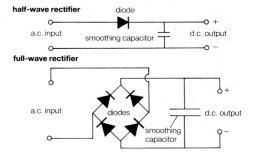

half-wave rectifier

diode

a.c. input   smoothing capacitor   d.c. output

full-wave rectifier

a.c. input   diodes   d.c. output

smoothing capacitor

full-wave rectifier a rectifier circuit (↑) in which current (p.103) flows during the whole of the oscillation (p.35) of the alternating current (p.125).

smoothing capacitor a capacitor (p.101) used to turn the series of bursts of current (p.103) produced by a rectifier circuit (↑) into a steady direct current (p.125). Charge (p.95) is stored in the capacitor during the bursts of current and then released during the time spaces between them.

semiconductor (*n*) a material that has a resistivity
(p.110) between that of a conductor (p.96) and
that of an insulator (p.97). Charge (p.95) flows
through a pure semiconductor carried by
electrons (p.139) and by holes (↓). The electrons
gain the energy they need to go from the valence
band (p.142) to the conduction band (p.142)
from the thermal (p.181) motion of the atoms
(p.139). At higher temperatures (p.181), the
number of charge carriers increases rapidly, so
pure semiconductors have a negative
temperature coefficient of resistance (p.110).
The elements (p.139) germanium and silicon are
important semiconductors.

n-type semiconductor

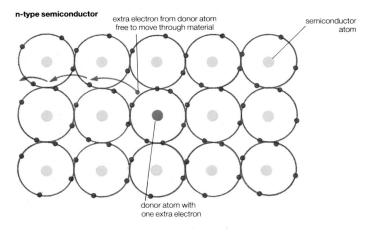

extra electron from donor atom
free to move through material

semiconductor
atom

donor atom with
one extra electron

n-type semiconductor a semiconductor (↑)
which has been doped (↓) with pentavalent
(p.140) atoms (p.139). These atoms each make
four covalent bonds (p.221) with the atoms of
the semiconductor, but the last valence electron
(p.140) is so weakly held in place that even the
smallest thermal (p.181) motion sets it free to
carry charge (p.95) through the semiconductor.
donor atom a pentavalent (p.140) atom (p.139)
which provides the charge (p.95) carriers in an
n-type semiconductor (↑).

p-type semiconductor

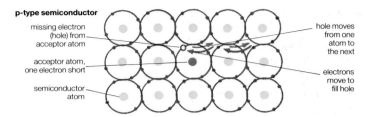

missing electron (hole) from acceptor atom

acceptor atom, one electron short

semiconductor atom

hole moves from one atom to the next

electrons move to fill hole

p-type semiconductor a semiconductor (↑) that has been doped (↓) with trivalent (p.140) atoms (p.139). These atoms each make three covalent bonds (p.221) with the atoms of the semiconductor, but have one electron (p.139) less than the number needed to make the usual four covalent bonds in the semiconductor's lattice (p.229). This electron can be taken from a nearby atom of the semiconductor, which in turn takes it from another semiconductor atom, the whole effect being of a positive charge (p.95) carrier moving through the semiconductor.

acceptor atom a trivalent (p.140) atom (p.139) which produces the holes (↓) which act as charge (p.95) carriers in a p-type semiconductor (↑).

hole (n) an imaginary positive charge (p.95) carrier caused by a missing electron (p.139) in the valence band (p.142) of a semiconductor (↑). Holes can be thought of as carrying the current (p.103) in p-type semiconductors (↑), though in fact it is electrons which are moving.

dope (v) to include a small amount of another element (p.139) in a semiconductor (↑). The number of atoms (p.139) used in doping is very small: only about one atom in 10^7 will be an atom of the doping element, so great care is needed to make sure that the semiconductor is very pure before it is doped.

intrinsic semiconductor a pure semiconductor (↑), one which has not been doped (↑).

extrinsic semiconductor a semiconductor (↑) which has been doped (↑), so is either a p-type (↑) or an n-type (↑).

pn junction two pieces of semiconductor (p.132), one p-type (p.133) and one n-type (p.132), joined together, or a single piece of semiconductor which has been doped (p.133) to make a p-type area and an n-type area, with these areas touching each other. The electrons (p.139) from the n-type area diffuse (p.190) into the p-type area, where they fill some of the holes (p.133), and holes from the p-type area diffuse into the n-type area where they are filled by electrons. This produces an area, called the depletion layer (↓), where there are no charge (p.95) carriers. When the p-type area is made negative and the n-type area is made positive, more charge carriers are pulled away from the pn junction, so no current (p.103) can flow. When the p-type area is made positive and the n-type area is made negative, charge carriers flow across the depletion layer as an electric current.

depletion layer the area of a pn junction (↑) where there are no charge (p.95) carriers because all the holes (p.133) have been filled by free electrons (p.139).

diode (*n*) any object which allows current (p.103) to flow in one direction only.

semiconductor diode a pn junction (↑) used to allow a current (p.103) to flow through it in one direction only.

forward biased of a pn junction (↑) connected (p.104) into a circuit (p.104) in the direction to conduct (p.96) electricity.

reverse biased of a pn junction (↑) connected (p.104) into a circuit (p.104) in the direction not to conduct (p.96) electricity.

pn junction

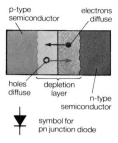

symbol for
pn junction diode

forward biased

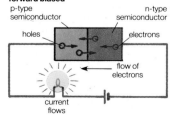

reverse biased

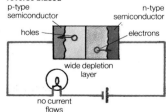

thermionic emission the release of electrons
(p.139) when a metal is heated. At high
temperatures (p.181), the thermal (p.181)
vibrations (p.242) of the atoms (p.139) become
strong enough for some of the free electrons
(p.139) in the metal to be thrown out. The
number of electrons given off rises very quickly
with the temperature of the metal, which is
usually in the form of a filament (p.82) heated by
the flow of current (p.103) through it.

space charge the cloud of electrons (p.139)
around an electrode (p.113) which is giving off
electrons by thermionic emission (↑).

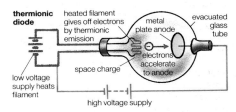

thermionic diode an evacuated (p.242) container
with a cathode (p.113) which is heated so it gives
off electrons (p.139) by thermionic emission (↑),
and an anode (p.113) which is not heated. When
the anode is given a positive charge (p.95), the
electrons from the space charge (↑) are
attracted (p.239) to the anode and a current
(p.103) can flow. When the anode is negatively
charged, no current can flow as the anode
cannot give off any electrons.

saturation² (n) the state of a thermionic diode (↑)
where the largest possible current (p.103) is
flowing between the anode (p.113) and the
cathode (p.113). When the potential difference
(p.107) between the (positive) anode and the
cathode is increased, the current cannot
increase without limit, because only a certain
number of electrons (p.139) are being given off
by thermionic emission (↑).

cathode rays an old name for the beam of
electrons (p.139) given off by the cathode
(p.113) of an electron gun (p.136).

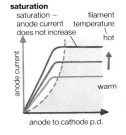

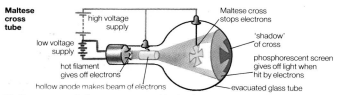

Maltese cross tube

high voltage supply

low voltage supply

hot filament gives off electrons

hollow anode makes beam of electrons

Maltese cross stops electrons

'shadow' of cross

phosphorescent screen gives off light when hit by electrons

evacuated glass tube

Maltese cross tube an evacuated (p.242)
container with a heated cathode (p.113) and an
anode (p.113) with a hole (p.133) in it. Some of
the electrons (p.139) that go through the hole in
the anode hit a metal cross. Those that miss the
cross hit a phosphor (↓) covered screen (p.242).
This shows that the electrons travel in straight
lines from the cathode if their path is not bent by
an electric field (p.97) or a magnetic field (p.92).

phosphor (n) a material that gives off light when hit
by electrons (p.139).

electron gun a system of electrodes (p.113) for
making a beam of electrons (p.139). In its
simplest form it has a heated filament (p.82), a
cathode (p.113), and an anode (p.113) with a
hole through which some electrons pass. It may
also have other electrodes to form the electrons
into a narrow beam and to control the number of
electrons in the beam.

Perrin tube

filament

evacuated glass tube

hollow tube

beam of electrons

S

magnet

N

low voltage supply

high voltage supply

anode

phosphorescent screen

electroscope shows charge on electrons

Perrin tube an evacuated (p.242) container with
an electron gun (↑) at one end, and a phosphor
(↑) covered screen (p.242) at the other. Just
above the screen is a hollow metal electrode
(p.113) with an open end into which the beam
can be directed using a magnetic field (p.92).
This electrode can be connected to an electroscope (p.97), so the charge on the 'cathode
rays' (p.135) can be shown to be negative.

fine beam tube

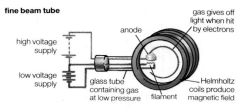

high voltage supply

low voltage supply

anode

gas gives off light when hit by electrons

glass tube containing gas at low pressure

filament

Helmholtz coils produce magnetic field

fine beam tube a glass container filled with gas
under low pressure (p.30), and containing an
electron gun (↑). The gas is ionized (p.139) by
the electrons (p.139) hitting it, and gives off light.
In this way, the path of the electron beam can be
seen. A fine beam tube also shows that electrons
in a magnetic field (p.92) move in circles if the
magnetic field is at 90° to the direction of motion
of the electrons.

cathode ray tube

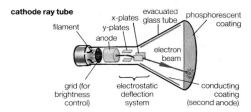

filament

x-plates
y-plates
anode

evacuated glass tube

phosphorescent coating

electron beam

grid (for brightness control)

electrostatic deflection system

conducting coating (second anode)

cathode ray tube an evacuated (p.242) container
with an electron gun (↑) at one end, and a
phosphor (↑) covered screen (p.242) at the
other. It also contains a system for bending the
electron (p.139) beam so that it can be made to
hit any point on the screen. This can be done
electrostatically (p.95), as is usual in a cathode
ray oscilloscope (p.138), or magnetically (p.90),
as is usual in a television. **c.r.t.** (*abbr*).

x-plates (*n,pl*) the metal plates in a cathode ray
tube (↑) with electrostatic deflection (p.138),
which move the beam of electrons (p.139) to the
right or left.

y-plates (*n,pl*) the metal plates in a cathode ray
tube (↑) with electrostatic deflection (p.138),
which move the beam of electrons (p.139) up or
down.

cathode ray oscilloscope an instrument for measuring how voltages (p.107) change with time. The signal (p.242) to be measured is fed through an amplifier (p.242) to the y-plates (p.137) of a cathode ray tube (p.137), while a timebase (↓) is fed to the x-plates (p.137). The oscilloscope then produces a graph of voltage against time. For other uses, the timebase can be changed for a second voltage, fed through an amplifier to the x-plates, so the change of one voltage with another can be seen directly. **c.r.o.** (*abbr*). Also known as **oscilloscope**.

oscilloscope (*n*) = cathode ray oscilloscope (↑).

timebase (*n*) a voltage (p.107) which changes linearly (p.234) with time, before suddenly returning to its starting value and repeating the process. This voltage is fed to the x-plates (p.137) in a cathode ray oscilloscope (↑).

electrostatic deflection a system for bending the electron (↓) beam in a cathode ray tube (p.137), using an electric field (p.97). Two pairs of parallel metal plates are used, at 90° to each other. One pair is called the x-plates (p.137) and bends the beam right and left; the other pair is called the y-plates (p.137) and bends the beam up and down. When one of the plates is given a positive charge (p.95) and the plate opposite to it is given a negative charge, the electric field causes the beam to be pulled towards the positive plate.

magnetic deflection a system for bending the electron (↓) beam in a cathode ray tube (p.137) using magnetic fields (p.92). These are usually made by electromagnets (p.115) around the outside of the c.r.t. The beam is bent in a direction at 90° to the magnetic field (*see Fleming's left-hand rule* (p.116)). In a television, two timebase (↑) voltages (p.107) are used, with two sets of coils (p.115) at 90° to each other. The first field causes the beam to sweep out a line from left to right. The second, slower, timebase moves the beam down slightly before the next line is produced. In this way the whole of the screen (p.242) is covered. The pattern is called a *raster*. The brightness of the beam is changed as the pattern is swept out, so producing a picture.

cathode ray oscilloscope

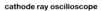
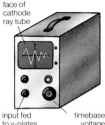

face of cathode ray tube

input fed to y-plates through amplifier

timebase voltage produced in oscilloscope and fed to x-plates

timebase voltage

time

electron (*n*) a fundamental particle (p.174) with a negative charge (p.95) of 1.6×10^{-19} coulomb (p.95) and a mass of 9.1×10^{-31}kg. It is thought that the electron is a point-like object which has no size. In atoms (↓), electrons are found around the nucleus (↓), arranged in shells (p.140).

electronic (*adj*) of a device which operates using complex circuits (p.104).

electronics (*n*) the study of electronic (↑) devices.

atom (*n*) one of the particles from which all matter is made. All atoms are made up of electrons (↑) around a nucleus (↓) which contains protons (p.155) and neutrons (p.155). The chemical (p.236) nature of the atom is controlled by the number of electrons in the atom and the charge (p.95) of the whole atom. The atom will be neutral (p.95) when the number of electrons is equal to the number of protons.

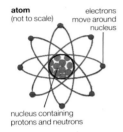

atom
(not to scale)

electrons
move around
nucleus

nucleus containing
protons and neutrons

element (*n*) any one of the different types of matter made from only one type of atom (↑). Atoms of the different elements are different in the number of protons (p.155) each contains, and so in the number of electrons (↑) needed to make a neutral (p.95) atom. It is the number and arrangement of the electrons in an atom which makes the different elements have different properties.

nucleus (*n*) the small positively charged central part of an atom (↑). The nucleus is about 10^4 to 10^5 times smaller than the atom, but as electrons are about 2000 times less massive than the protons (p.155) or neutrons (p.155) from which the nucleus is made, it contains almost all the mass of the atom. **nuclei** (*pl*), **nuclear** (*adj*).

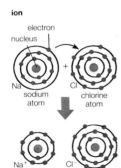

ion

electron

nucleus

Na
sodium
atom

Cl
chlorine
atom

Na⁺
sodium ion

Cl⁻
chlorine ion

ion (*n*) an atom (↑) which has more or less than the number of electrons (↑) needed to make it neutral (p.95). It therefore has an electric charge (p.95): positive (p.95) if there are too few electrons; negative (p.95) if there are too many.

ionize (*v*) to form ions (↑), particularly by collisions (p.22) of fast moving charged (p.95) particles. **ionization** (*n*).

first ionization energy the smallest energy which
is needed to remove one electron (p.139)
to an infinite distance from a neutral (p.95)
atom (p.139). It is a measure of how tightly
the outermost electron is held to the
atom.

shell (*n*) one of the basic layers into which an
electron (p.139) may be placed around an atom
(p.139). The *n*th shell from the centre of the atom
can hold $2n^2$ electrons. In any atom the
electrons fill up the shells in order until the
number of electrons is equal to the number of
protons (p.155) in the nucleus (p.139), so that
the atom is neutral (p.95). The arrangement of
electrons in the outer shell controls the chemical
(p.236) properties of the element (p.139).
Starting from the centre of the atom, the shells
are called the *K-shell*, *L-shell*, *M-shell*, etc.

valence shell the outer shell (↑) of an atom
(p.139). The number of electrons (p.139) in this
shell controls the chemical (p.236) properties of
the element (p.139).

valence electron any electron (p.139) which is in
the valence shell (↑) of an atom (p.139). A
valence electron can therefore be taken away or
shared with another atom easily. It is these
electrons which hold atoms together in solids
and compounds (p.236).

alkali metal an element (p.139) with only one
electron (p.139) in the valence shell (↑). Alkali
metals are all highly reactive (p.236); e.g. lithium,
sodium.

noble gas an element (p.139) with a full valence
shell (↑). They are all unreactive (p.236); e.g.
neon, argon.

trivalent (*adj*) of an atom (p.139) having three
valence electrons (↑).

pentavalent (*adj*) of an atom (p.139) having five
valence electrons (↑).

orbital (*n*) a way of describing the probability
(p.235) of finding an electron (p.139) at a
particular place in an atom (p.139). In quantum
mechanics (p.150), an electron is not described
by its position in a shell (↑), but by the probability
of finding it at a particular place.

first ionization energy

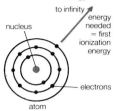

shell

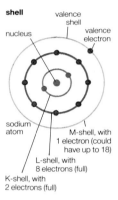

Pauli exclusion principle no two electrons
(p.139) can ever be in the same state, e.g. in the
same orbital (↑) and with the same spin (↓). This
means that in any atom (p.139), each orbital can
contain only two electrons, one with spin up and
one with spin down.

spin (*n*) a property of electrons (p.139) and some
other fundamental particles (p.174) which behave
as if they had built-in angular momentum (p.25).
This angular momentum is always the same for a
certain type of particle and is always a whole
number times $h/4\pi$, where h is Planck's constant
(p.149). The laws of quantum mechanics (p.150)
state that the component (p.233) of the spin
angular momentum in any direction can take only
certain values. For an electron there are only two
possible values: spin up and spin down.

periodic table a table in which the elements
(p.139) are placed in order of atomic number
(p.155). A new line is begun in the table when a
new shell (↑) begins to fill, so elements which
have similar chemical (p.236) properties appear
in the same parts of the table.

band theory of solids

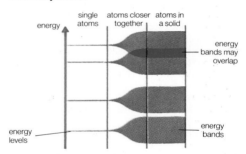

band theory of solids a way of using quantum
mechanics (p.150) to describe the behaviour of
solids. When many atoms (p.139) are placed
close together, as they are in a solid, the
energies of the orbitals (↑) change slightly, so
single energy levels become ranges of energy,
called energy bands (p.142).

energy band a range of energies which can be taken by an electron (p.132) in a solid. The pattern of energy bands in a solid is similar to the pattern of energy levels (↓) in a single atom (p.139) of the same material.

valence band the energy band (↑) in which the valence electrons (p.140) of a material are found.

conduction band an energy band (↑) in which there are both electrons (p.139) and spaces for more electrons. To move through a material, an electron needs to gain energy. Because of the Pauli exclusion principle (p.141), it can do this only if there is an empty energy level (↓) into which it can move. Materials which have a conduction band are the only ones which can conduct (p.96) electricity at low temperatures.

forbidden band a range of energies between two energy bands (↑). No electron (p.139) can have one of these energies, and an electron can cross from one energy band to the next only if the band gap (↓) is very small. If the material has a small band gap, the thermal energy (p.18) of the electron may be enough for it to cross the band gap. Such materials are called semiconductors (p.132).

band gap the energy between the top of the valence band (↑) and the bottom of the next higher energy band (↑). If the valence band is full, the material will be able to conduct electricity only if the band gap is very small. In some materials the valence band and the next higher energy band overlap, so there is no band gap. The material will thus be a good conductor even if the valence band is full.

band gap

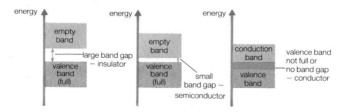

energy level

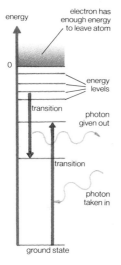

energy level any of the orbitals (p.140) in an atom (p.139) into which an electron (p.139) can be placed, together with a measure of the energy that the electron will have in that orbital compared to the energy it would have if it were infinitely distant from the atom, with no kinetic energy (p.18).

transition (*n*) the moving of an electron (p.139) from one energy level (↑) to another. When a transition takes place, energy equal to the energy difference between the two levels must also be taken in or given out. This usually takes the form of a photon (p.148) whose frequency (p.36) is such that it carries the correct amount of energy.

ground state the state of an atom (p.139) when all its electrons (p.139) are in the lowest possible energy levels (↑).

excited (*adj*) of an atom (p.139) or electron (p.139) not in its ground state (↑).

hydrogen spectrum because an atom (p.139) of the element (p.139) hydrogen contains only one electron (p.139), its emission spectrum (p.81) is quite simple. It is made up of a number of lines, whose frequencies (p.36) are given by $Rc(1/n^2 - 1/m^2)$, where n and m are whole numbers, c is the speed of light (p.59), and R is a constant (p.234), called the Rydberg constant (p.144). $R = 1.097 \times 10^7 \text{m}^{-1}$

hydrogen spectrum

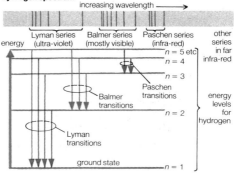

principal quantum number a whole number describing the energy level (p.143) of an electron (p.139) in the Bohr model of the hydrogen atom ($\downarrow$). For the ground state (p.143) the principal quantum number is one. In the equation for the hydrogen spectrum (p.143), $Rc(1/n^2 - 1/m^2)$, n and m are the principal quantum numbers of the two energy levels between which an electron moves in that transition (p.143).

Rydberg constant the constant (p.234) R in the equation for the hydrogen spectrum (p.143), $Rc(1/n^2 - 1/m^2)$.

Bohr model of the hydrogen atom a description of the energy levels (p.143) in hydrogen and the spectrum (p.80) they produce. It is based on these ideas: electrons (p.139) orbit (p.26) the nucleus (p.139) in circles, but can be in orbits only where their angular momentum (p.25) is a whole number times Planck's constant (p.149); the electrons do not give off electromagnetic (p.115) radiation (p.241) as they move in these orbits, but only when they move from one orbit to another. (They would be expected to give off such radiation because they are accelerating (p.12).) An electron moving from one orbit to another gives off or takes in a single photon (p.148) with a frequency (p.36) equal to the energy change between the two orbits, divided by Planck's constant. These ideas lead to a value for the Rydberg constant ($\uparrow$) which agrees very well with the value found in experiments.

Lyman series the lines in the hydrogen spectrum (p.143) which have $n = 1$ in the equation $Rc(1/n^2 - 1/m^2)$. They are produced by transitions (p.143) between excited (p.143) states (p.192) and the ground state (p.143). These lines are in the ultra-violet (p.89) part of the electromagnetic spectrum (p.86).

Balmer series the lines in the hydrogen spectrum (p.143) which have $n = 2$ in the equation $Rc(1/n^2 - 1/m^2)$. They are produced by transitions (p.143) between higher excited (p.143) states (p.192) and the first excited state. These lines are in the visible (p.88) part of the electromagnetic spectrum (p.86).

Bohr model of the hydrogen atom

angular momentum of electron in orbit = $\dfrac{nh}{2\pi}$

Bohr radius

$n = 5$
$n = 4$
$n = 3$
$n = 2$
$n = 1$

Paschen transitions

Lyman transitions

Balmer transitions

Paschen series the lines in the hydrogen spectrum (p.143) which have $n = 3$ in the equation $Rc(1/n^2 - 1/m^2)$. They are produced by transitions (p.143) between higher excited (p.143) states (p.192) and the second excited state. These lines are in the infra-red (p.88) part of the electromagnetic spectrum (p.86).

Bohr radius the radius of the ground state (p.143) orbit (p.26) in the Bohr model of the hydrogen atom ($\uparrow$).

lines in absorption and emission spectra all the lines which are present in an absorption spectrum (p.81) are also found in the emission spectrum (p.81) of the same element (p.139), since the transitions (p.143) can happen either from higher to lower energy, giving off a photon (p.148), or from lower to higher energy, taking in a photon. But there are some other lines in the emission spectrum. This is because transitions in the absorption spectrum must involve the ground state (p.143), as almost all electrons (p.139) will be in the ground state before a photon is taken in. But an excited (p.143) atom (p.139) may return to the ground state through one or more other states, giving off more than one photon.

lines in absorption and emission spectra

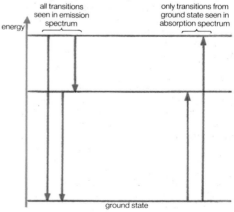

energy

all transitions seen in emission spectrum

only transitions from ground state seen in absorption spectrum

ground state

Franck-Hertz experiment

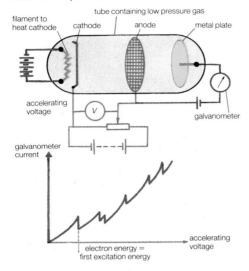

Franck-Hertz experiment an experiment which
shows that atoms (p.139) have energy levels
(p.143). Electrons (p.139) are accelerated (p.12)
by an electric field (p.97) in a container holding a
gas or vapour (p.195) at low pressure (p.30). The
electrons are then slowed down by a second
electric field in the opposite direction to the first
one. The electrons reach the last electrode
(p.113) only if they have not lost any energy by
collisions (p.22) with the atoms in the container.
The results show that the collisions are all elastic
(p.224) until the first excitation energy (↓) is
reached. At this energy the electrons gain
enough energy from the accelerating electric
field to move the atoms in the tube from their
ground state (p.143) to their first excited (p.143)
state.

first excitation energy the lowest energy needed
to move an electron (p.139) in a given type of
atom (p.139) from its ground state (p.143) into
an excited (p.143) state.

photoelectric effect

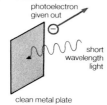

photoelectron given out

short wavelength light

clean metal plate

Einstein's explanation of the photoelectric effect

photon energy = frequency x Planck's constant

energy of photoelectrons for all materials, gradient = Planck's constant

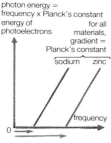

sodium   zinc

frequency

0

minimum frequency = work function / Planck's constant

photoelectric effect the effect by which some metals give off electrons (p.139) when light falls on them. For a given metal, the light must have a wavelength (p.43) shorter than a certain value. For most metals, ultra-violet (p.89) light must be used, but the alkali metals (p.140) will give off electrons when hit by light from the blue end of the visible spectrum (p.80).

photocathode (*n*) an electrode (p.113) which gives off electrons (p.139) when hit by light. It is usually covered with a material with a low work function (p.148), so electrons can be produced by light of longer wavelengths (p.43).

photoelectric cell any instrument which produces an electromotive force (p.105) or allows a current (p.103) to flow when light falls on it. A simple form of photoelectric cell is made from a photocathode (↑) placed in an evacuated (p.242) container with an anode (p.113) to collect the photoelectrons (p.148).

photoconductive cell a photoelectric cell (↑) which allows a current (p.103) to flow when light falls on it, but which produces no electromotive force (p.105) of its own.

Einstein's explanation of the photoelectric effect the energy of each electron (p.139) released by the photoelectric effect (↑) does not depend on the intensity (p.44) of the light, but increases with the frequency (p.36) of the light. An increase in intensity produces more electrons, but with similar energies. This was explained by saying that light comes in 'packs' called quanta (p.148). Each quantum carries a certain amount of energy and an electron given off in the photoelectric effect carries the energy of one quantum, less any energy that was used in escaping from the metal surface. A greater light intensity means more quanta, but each one still carries the same energy, while higher frequency light quanta carry more energy, so the photoelectrons (p.148) each carry more energy. The energy with which a photoelectron will leave the metal surface is $hf - \phi$, where h is Planck's constant (p.149), f is the frequency of the light, and ϕ is the work function (p.148).

work function the smallest amount of energy that
a photon (↓) must carry to produce a
photoelectron (↓) from a given metal.

photoelectron (*n*) an electron (p.139) given off by
the photoelectric effect (p.147).

quantum (*n*) the smallest amount of matter or
energy that there can be. The size of a quantum
varies. E.g. electromagnetic waves (p.59) come
in quanta called photons (↓). The energy carried
by each photon depends on the frequency (p.36)
of the light, but light of a given frequency can
never carry an energy less than the energy of a
single quantum of that frequency, and the
number of quanta present must always be a
whole number. **quanta** (*pl*).

photon (*n*) a quantum (↑) of an electromagnetic
wave (p.59). A photon has an energy of *hf*, where
f is the frequency (p.36) and *h* is Planck's
constant (↓).

stopping potential the potential difference (p.107)
by which the anode (p.113) in a photoelectric cell
(p.147) must be made more negative than the
photocathode (p.147) if no photoelectrons (↑)
are to reach it. This potential multiplied by the
charge (p.95) on an electron (p.139) is equal to
the kinetic energy (p.18) with which the electrons
leave the photocathode. This in turn is equal to
the difference between the energy of each
quantum (↑) of light and the work function (↑) of
the material of the photocathode.

stopping potential

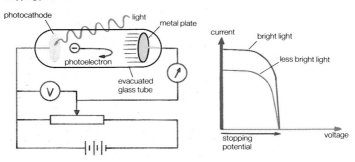

electronvolt (*n*) a unit (p.8) of energy which is equal to the energy gained or lost by an electron (p.139) when it moves through a potential difference (p.107) of one volt (p.107). $1 eV = 1.6 \times 10^{-19} J$. **eV** (*abbr*).

photomultiplier

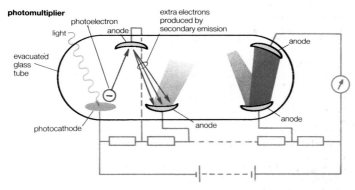

photomultiplier (*n*) an instrument in which the production of a single photoelectron (↑) can cause a large current (p.103). This can be used to detect very small amounts of light. The photoelectron from the photocathode (p.147) is accelerated (p.12) towards an anode (p.113) which is covered with a material which gives off electrons (p.139) easily when hit by other electrons. These electrons are then accelerated towards another anode at a higher electric potential (p.98) than the first, where a larger number of electrons are again given off. This action is repeated several more times, so a single photoelectron, produced by a single photon (↑), may produce a very large number of electrons, resulting in a large current when these electrons arrive at the last anode.

secondary emission the release of several electrons (p.139) from a material when it is hit by a single, high energy, electron.

Planck's constant a fundamental constant (p.234), *h* in equations. It is a measure of the size of quantum (↑) effects. $h = 6.6 \times 10^{-34} J s$.

quantum mechanics that part of physics which has to do with systems where it is important to understand that energy (p.17) and matter come in quanta (p.148) rather than continuously. Also known as **quantum physics**.

quantum physics = quantum mechanics (↑).

Schrödinger equation the basic equation of non-relativistic (p.34) quantum mechanics (↑). It describes the behaviour of a wavefunction (↓) which contains all the information that can be known about a particular system.

wavefunction (*n*) a quantity which contains all the information that can be known about a system. It contains information about the phase (p.37) of the wave (p.42) that is linked to any particle (*see wave-particle duality* (p.152)) and about the probability (p.235) of finding the particle at that point. The Schrödinger equation (↑) controls exactly the form of the wavefunction, but the wavefunction gives information only on the probability of finding an object in a certain state (p.192).

wavefunction　　　　　**Heisenberg's uncertainty principle**

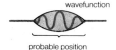

wavefunction

probable position

wavefunction

probable position

uncertainty in position: small
uncertainty in wavelength (momentum): large

wavefunction

probable position
uncertainty in position: large
uncertainty in wavelength (momentum): small

Heisenberg's uncertainty principle a statement of the fact that in quantum mechanics (↑) it is not possible to know everything about a system exactly, no matter how accurate (p.240) your instruments. It is usually stated in one of two forms: (1) $\Delta p\,\Delta x \geqslant h/2\pi$, where Δx is the uncertainty in measurement of the position of an object, Δp is the uncertainty in measurement of its momentum (p.21) and h is Planck's constant (p.149); and (2) $\Delta E\,\Delta t \geqslant h/2\pi$, where ΔE is the uncertainty in the measurement of the energy of the object, and Δt is the uncertainty in the time at which the energy was measured.

Heisenberg's microscope experiment

observer

microscope

light diffracts

long wavelength light

particle

uncertainty in position: large
uncertainty in momentum: small

observer

microscope

short wavelength light

particle moves when hit by light

uncertainty in momentum: large
uncertainty in position: small

antiparticle

Heisenberg's microscope experiment a thought experiment (p.238) in which an object is viewed through a microscope (p.74) to discover its position as exactly as possible. This can only be measured accurately (p.240) if light of a short enough wavelength (p.43) is used. Since the photons (p.148) reflected (p.45) into the microscope will give the object some momentum (p.21), it is not possible to know both the position and the momentum completely accurately.

quantum number a number which describes one of the different states of a system. E.g. the different allowed orbits (p.26) of an electron (p.139) in the Bohr model of the hydrogen atom (p.144) have different quantum numbers, as do the two possible spin (p.141) states of an electron.

fermion (n) any particle which has a spin (p.141) which is an odd number multiplied by $h/4\pi$, where h is Planck's constant (p.149); e.g. an electron (p.139).

boson (n) any particle whose spin (p.141) is a whole number multiplied by $h/2\pi$, where h is Planck's constant (p.149); e.g. a photon (p.148).

particle		antiparticle	
electron	• e^-	positron	• e^+
proton	● p	antiproton	● $\bar{p}$
neutron	● n	antineutron	● $\bar{n}$
photon is its own antiparticle ∿∿			γ

antiparticle (n) a particle which has the same mass as some other particle but opposite quantum numbers (↑), including charge (p.95). Every particle has an antiparticle, but some particles, e.g. the photon (p.148), are their own antiparticle. When a particle meets its antiparticle, they may destroy each other, producing energy in the form of lighter particles or two (or more) photons.

antimatter (n) matter made from particles which are antiparticles (↑) to the particles from which matter is usually made.

positron (n) the antiparticle (↑) to the electron (p.139).

wave-particle duality

	wave-like behaviour	particle-like behaviour
light	interference	photoelectric effect
electrons	electron diffraction	charge on a single electron

wave-particle duality the ability of waves (p.42) to show some of the properties of particles and of particles to show some of the properties of waves. E.g. light waves behave like particles in the photoelectric effect (p.147), while electrons (p.139) behave like waves in electron diffraction (↓). Wave-particle duality is a result of quantum mechanics (p.150).

de Broglie's hypothesis the idea that waves (p.42) can behave like particles and particles like waves. E.g. a wave of frequency (p.36) f behaving like a particle of energy hf, and a particle of momentum (p.21) p behaving like a wave of wavelength (p.43) h/p, where h is Planck's constant (p.149).

de Broglie wavelength the wavelength (p.43) a particle seems to have when it behaves like a wave (p.42) (*see wave-particle duality* (↑)). $\lambda = h/p$, where λ is the de Broglie wavelength, p is the momentum (p.21) of the particle, and h is Planck's constant (p.149).

electron diffraction

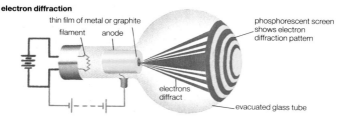

thin film of metal or graphite

filament   anode

phosphorescent screen shows electron diffraction pattern

electrons diffract

evacuated glass tube

electron diffraction the diffraction (p.50) of electrons (p.139), which behave like waves (p.42) because of wave-particle duality (↑). This cannot be seen when electrons pass through a narrow opening or diffraction grating (p.80), as the de Broglie wavelength (↑) of an electron is very small even when it has been accelerated (p.12) through only a small potential difference (p.107) and so has little momentum (p.21). Crystalline (p.229) solids have atoms (p.139) arranged in a regular pattern, which acts like a very small diffraction grating. When electrons are fired through a thin layer of metal or carbon in the form of graphite, a diffraction pattern (p.51) is produced. The wavelength (p.43) producing the pattern can be found if the spacing of the atoms in the solid is known; the results agree with de Broglie's hypothesis (↑).

neutron diffraction the diffraction (p.50) of neutrons (p.155), which behave like waves (p.42) because of wave-particle duality (↑). Because neutrons are not charged (p.95), the diffraction of neutrons from a solid depends on the nature of that solid in a different way from the diffraction of electrons (p.139). To get neutrons with a long enough de Broglie wavelength (↑), very slow moving neutrons are used.

photon pressure the pressure (p.30) produced on an object when it is hit by light. Each photon (p.148) carries a momentum (p.21) h/λ, where h is Planck's constant (p.149), and λ is the wavelength (p.43) of the light. If a photon is absorbed (p.242) or reflected (p.42), the impulse (p.21) produced results in a force equal to the change in momentum of each photon multiplied by the number of photons per second striking the surface.

Compton effect when an X-ray (p.89) photon (p.148) hits an electron (p.139), the electron may move off and the photon continue with a longer wavelength (p.43). The change in wavelength is exactly what would be expected from the law of conservation of momentum (p.21) and the idea of photons carrying momentum as in de Broglie's hypothesis (↑).

Compton effect

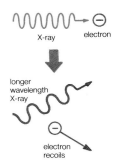

X-ray

electron

longer wavelength X-ray

electron recoils

size of nucleus for a nucleus (p.139) of mass number ($\downarrow$) A, the radius of the nucleus is about $1.1 \times 10^{-15} A^{1/3}$ m.

currant-bun model of the atom an old model of the atom (p139) which supposed that the atom was made up of a sphere of positive charge (p.95) of about the same size as the whole atom, with electrons (p.139) set into this sphere. This idea was disproved by the Geiger-Marsden experiment ($\downarrow$).

Rutherford model of the atom a model in which the electrons (p.139) move in orbits (p.26) around a small positively charged (p.95) nucleus (p.139). This model was proved to be correct by the results of the Geiger-Marsden experiment ($\downarrow$).

currant-bun model of the atom

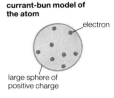

electron

large sphere of positive charge

Rutherford model of the atom

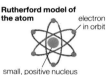

electron in orbit

small, positive nucleus

Geiger-Marsden experiment

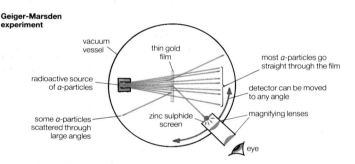

vacuum vessel

thin gold film

radioactive source of a-particles

most a-particles go straight through the film

detector can be moved to any angle

some a-particles scattered through large angles

zinc sulphide screen

magnifying lenses

eye

Geiger-Marsden experiment an experiment in which a-particles (p.158) were fired at a thin gold sheet (a foil) in an evacuated (p.242) container. Most of the a-particles went straight through the foil, but a few were bent through large angles, as they had experienced a large force. This supported the Rutherford model of the atom ($\uparrow$) rather than the currant-bun model of the atom ($\uparrow$), as the atoms must have contained a large amount of charge (p.95) in a small volume (p.55) if the a-particle paths were to be so strongly bent.

Rutherford scattering the behaviour of a-particles (p.158) found in the Geiger-Marsden experiment ($\uparrow$).

atomic number the number of protons ($\downarrow$) in a nucleus (p.139). As the charge (p.95) on a proton is exactly equal and opposite to that on an electron (p.139), the atomic number is equal to the number of electrons needed to make a neutral (p.95) atom (p.139). It is this which controls the chemical (p.236) properties of the atom, so atoms with different atomic numbers are atoms of different elements (p.139).

mass number the number of nucleons ($\downarrow$) in a nucleus (p.139). As neutrons ($\downarrow$) and protons ($\downarrow$) have nearly the same mass (p.8), the mass number is about equal to the relative atomic mass ($\downarrow$) of the atom. The mass number is shown in equations by the symbol A, and is written to the top left of the chemical symbol (p.236) of the element, e.g. ^{208}Pb. Also known as **nucleon number**.

nucleon number = mass number ($\uparrow$).

relative atomic mass the mass (p.8) of an atom (p.139), measured in units (p.8) where the mass of an atom of ^{12}C is 12.0000. Also known as **atomic weight**. **r.a.m.** (abbr).

atomic weight = relative atomic mass ($\uparrow$).

atomic mass unit the unit (p.8) in which relative atomic mass ($\uparrow$) is measured. **a.m.u.** (abbr).

proton (n) the positively charged (p.95) particle found in nuclei (p.139). It has a mass of 1.673×10^{-27}kg, and a charge of 1.6×10^{-19}C, exactly equal and opposite to that of the electron (p.139).

neutron (n) the neutral (p.95) particle found in nuclei (p.139). It has a mass of 1.675×10^{-27}kg. Although it has no charge (p.95), it has a magnetic moment (p.93) which suggests that it is made up of charged particles (see quarks (p.176)).

nucleon (n) the name given to any of the particles found in a nucleus (p.139), i.e. a proton ($\uparrow$) or a neutron ($\uparrow$).

nuclide (n) a nucleus (p.139) containing a particular number of neutrons ($\uparrow$) and protons ($\uparrow$). The atomic number ($\uparrow$), Z, is written to the bottom left of the chemical symbol (p.236) of the element (p.139), X, while the mass number ($\uparrow$), A, is written to the top left, $^{A}_{Z}X$.

neutron number the number of neutrons (p.155) in a nucleus (p.139). The neutron number is equal to the difference between the mass number (p.155) and the atomic number (p.155).

isotope

$^{35}_{17}$ Cl	$^{37}_{17}$ Cl	isotopes of chlorine
17 protons	17 protons	same number of protons
18 neutrons	20 neutrons	different number of neutrons

isotope (*n*) any one of a series of nuclides (p.155) having the same atomic number (p.155), but different mass numbers (p.155). Isotopes have the same atomic numbers, so have the same chemical (p.236) properties, but different numbers of neutrons (p.155).

mass spectrometer an instrument which separates nuclei (p.139) or other charged (p.95) particles of different mass (p.8). It works by selecting particles of a given speed, using electric fields (p.97) and magnetic fields (p.92) at 90° to each other. These fields will have no effect on particles of the chosen speed, but other particles will be forced out of the instrument. The chosen particles then pass through another magnetic field, and the radius of the path they follow allows their mass to be found.

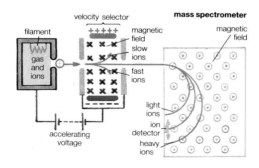

mass defect

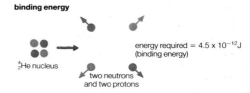

	$^4_2$He nucleus	mass = 6.6502×10^{-27}kg
	two neutrons and two protons	total mass = 6.7000×10^{-27}kg
		mass defect = 4.98×10^{-29}kg

mass defect the difference in mass (p.8) between the neutrons (p.155) and protons (p.155) of which a nuclide (p.155) is made, and the mass of the nuclide itself. It is caused by the loss of energy (and so mass) which would be released if a nucleus was made from free neutrons and protons. It is equal to the binding energy ($\downarrow$) divided by the square of the speed of light (p.59).

binding energy

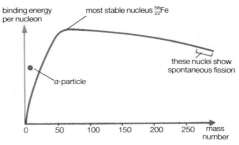

energy required = 4.5×10^{-12}J (binding energy)

$^4_2$He nucleus

two neutrons and two protons

binding energy the energy which is needed to break a nuclide (p.155) apart into neutrons (p.155) and protons (p.155), all infinitely far apart.
binding energy per nucleon the binding energy ($\uparrow$) of a nuclide (p.155) divided by its mass number (p.155). It is a measure of how tightly the nucleons (p.155) in that nuclide are held together.

binding energy per nucleon

binding energy per nucleon

most stable nucleus $^{56}_{22}$Fe

these nuclei show spontaneous fission

α-particle

0   50   100   150   200   250   mass number

radioactive (*adj*) of a nuclide (p.155) that can change into another nuclide, giving off one or more other particles, usually α- ($\downarrow$), β- ($\downarrow$) or γ- (p.160) particles. This is not varied by changing the conditions of the nuclide, e.g. temperature, pressure, etc., nor by how much time a particular nuclide has had to decay ($\downarrow$). **radioactivity** (*n*).

radioisotope (*n*) a radioactive ($\uparrow$) nuclide (p.155).

decay (*v,n*) the act of a radioactive ($\uparrow$) nuclide (p.155) changing into another nuclide, which may also be radioactive, but need not be.

naturally occurring of a nuclide (p.155) which is found in nature. Such nuclides are usually stable (p.236), or have half-lives (p.162) which are long compared to the age of the Earth, but they may be short-lived daughter nuclides ($\downarrow$) from an unstable nuclide with a long half-life which is also naturally occurring.

daughter nuclide a nuclide (p.155) produced in a radioactive ($\uparrow$) decay ($\uparrow$).

α-particle (*n*) a particle given off in some radio-active ($\uparrow$) decays ($\uparrow$). It is a nucleus (p.139) of ^{4}He, made of two protons (p.155) and two neutrons (p.155). Because α-particles have a particularly high binding energy per nucleon (p.155) for their size, they are given off instead of separate neutrons and protons by any nucleus which has too many neutrons and protons to be stable (p.236). α-particles produce a large amount of ionization (p.139), so are stopped quickly in air, where they travel only a few centi-metres, and can pass through no more than a thin sheet of paper. When a nucleus gives off an α-particle, the mass number (p.155) of the nucleus decreases by four, and the atomic number (p.155) decreases by two. Also known as **alpha particle**.

α-particle

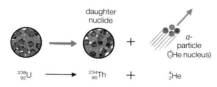

daughter nuclide

$+$

α-particle ($^4_2$He nucleus)

$^{238}_{92}$U $\longrightarrow$ $^{234}_{90}$Th $+$ $^4_2$He

**energy spectrum of
α-particles**

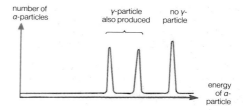

number of
α-particles

γ-particle
also produced

no γ-
particle

energy
of α-
particle

energy spectrum of α-particles a nuclide
(p.155) which gives off α-particles (↑), gives
them all off with the same energy, or with one of
a few separate energies, but not with a wide
spread of energies. If α-particles with more than
one energy are produced, there are also γ-
particles (p.160) produced with energies equal to
the difference between the energy of the α-
particle given off and the highest possible α-
particle energy, so the law of conservation of
energy (p.18) is obeyed.

β-particle (*n*) a particle given off in some
radioactive (↑) decays (↑). It is an electron
(p.139), given off by a nucleus (p.139) when a
neutron (p.155) in that nucleus turns into a
proton (p.155), giving off a β-particle and an
antineutrino (p.161). Nuclides (p.155) which have
too many neutrons for their atomic number
(p.155) give off β-particles. The atomic number
increases by one, while the mass number (p.155)
does not change. β-particles are able to pass
through thicker materials than α-particles (↑) as
they are less strongly ionizing (p.139), being able
to pass through aluminium sheets up to a few
millimetres thick. Also known as **beta particle**.

β-particle

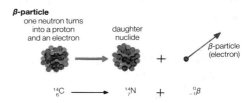

one neutron turns
into a proton
and an electron

daughter
nuclide

β-particle
(electron)

$^{14}_{6}C \longrightarrow {}^{14}_{7}N + {}^{\;0}_{-1}\beta$

energy spectrum of a β-particle

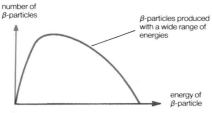

number of
β-particles

β-particles produced
with a wide range of
energies

energy of
β-particle

energy spectrum of β-particles β-particles
(p.159) are given off from a nucleus (p.139) with
a wide spread of energies. This shows that
another particle is given off at the same time as
the β-particle, otherwise the law of conservation
of energy (p.18) would be broken. This other
particle is an antineutrino (↓).

γ-particle (n) a particle given off in some
radioactive (p.158) decays (p.158). It is a photon
(p.148) with a short wavelength (p.43). It has no
mass and no charge (p.95). The atomic number
(p.155) and mass number (p.155) of a nucleus
(p.139) do not change when a γ-particle is given
off. γ-particles are usually produced by a nucleus
very soon after it has given off either an α-particle
(p.158) or a β-particle (p.159). As the nucleons
(p.155) left behind rearrange themselves, the
γ-particle carries away any remaining energy.
γ-particles are only weakly ionizing (p.139), so
can pass through thick layers of dense (p.28)
material, e.g. a few centimetres of lead. Also
known as **γ-ray** or **gamma particle**.

γ-ray (n) = γ-particle (↑).

γ-particle

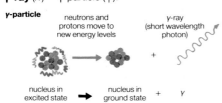

neutrons and
protons move to
new energy levels

γ-ray
(short wavelength
photon)

nucleus in
excited state ➡ nucleus in
ground state + γ

energy spectrum of γ-particles

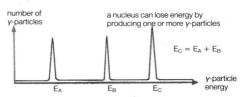

number of γ-particles

a nucleus can lose energy by producing one or more γ-particles

$E_C = E_A + E_B$

γ-particle energy

E_A E_B E_C

energy spectrum of γ-particles γ-particles ($\uparrow$) are given off with one of a few separate energies, like atoms (p.139) producing line spectra (p.81). This suggests that there are energy levels (p.143) inside the nucleus (p.139), as there are energy levels for electrons (p.139) in an atom.

neutrino (n) a particle given off in β^+-emission ($\downarrow$) and K-capture (p.162). It has no charge (p.95) and, it is thought, no mass. Neutrinos affect matter only very weakly. On average a neutrino can pass through matter for very long distances without having any effect, but in experiments in which large numbers of neutrinos are produced, a few of them can be seen. Different types of neutrinos are produced when decays (p.158) produce a lepton (p.174) other than an electron (p.139) or positron (p.151).

antineutrino (n) the antiparticle (p.151) of the neutrino ($\uparrow$). It is given off with an electron (p.139) when a neutron (p.155) turns into a proton (p.155).

β^+-emission (n) the giving off of a positron (p.151) and a neutrino ($\uparrow$) by a nucleus (p.139) when a proton (p.155) turns into a neutron (p.155). Free protons are lighter than free neutrons, so this can happen only in a nuclide (p.155) where there are too many protons for the number of neutrons. It still needs a lot of energy, so K-capture (p.162) is more usual in such nuclides.

β^+-emission

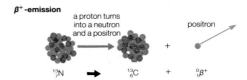

a proton turns into a neutron and a positron

positron

$^{13}_{7}N$ ➡ $^{13}_{6}C$ + $^{0}_{1}\beta^+$

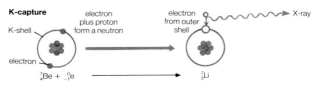

K-capture *(n)* the giving off of a neutrino (p.161) when a nuclide (p.155) which has too many protons (p.155) for its number of neutrons (p.155) takes an electron (p.139) from the inner shell (p.140) of electrons (called the K-shell) of the atom (p.139) and uses it to turn a proton into a neutron plus a neutrino. As the electron is replaced by others from further out in the atom, X-rays (p.89) are given off too.

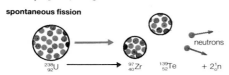

spontaneous fission the breaking of a nucleus (p.139) into two or more pieces of about equal size which takes place as a radioactive (p.158) decay. A particular nuclide (p.155) will not always break into the same pieces, and only the largest nuclides behave in this way. Since lighter nuclides contain fewer neutrons (p.155) per proton (p.155) than heavier ones, a number of neutrons will also be released.

half-life *(n)* the time taken for the number of radioactive (p.158) nuclides (p.155) of a particular type in a piece of radioactive material to reduce to one half of its original number. After two half-lives, the number of the original type of nuclide present will have fallen to one quarter of its original number and so on. If the daughter nuclide (p.158) is not radioactive, then the amount of radioactivity produced by the material will also be halved after one half-life, halved again after two half-lives, and so on. The half-life is equal to $(\ln 2)/\lambda$, where λ is the radioactive decay constant ($\downarrow$).

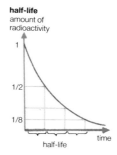

radioactive decay law if at time $t = 0$, there are N_0 radioactive (p.158) nuclides (p.155) present, then at time t, the number will be N, where $N = N_0\exp(-\lambda t)$, where λ is the radioactive decay constant ($\downarrow$).

radioactive decay constant the constant (p.234) λ in the radioactive decay law ($\uparrow$). $\lambda\delta t$ is the probability (p.235) of the nuclide (p.155) decaying in the short time δt.

random nature of radioactive decay the fact that there is no way of knowing when any particular nucleus (p.139) will decay (p.158), so where the number of nuclei decaying in a given time is small, the number of decays seen may vary at random (p.235), with the radioactive decay law ($\uparrow$) showing only the average number of decays in a given time.

background radiation

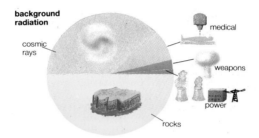

cosmic rays

medical

weapons

power

rocks

background radiation the radioactivity (p.158) that is always all around us. It is caused mostly by cosmic rays ($\downarrow$), and radioactivity from naturally occurring (p.158) radioisotopes (p.158), with small amounts from nuclear (p.139) weapons and other man-made causes. It varies around the world, being largest in areas of granite rock, in buildings with poor air flow, and underground, where radioisotopes which are gases can gradually increase. Radioactivity and X-rays (p.89) are also used on humans for medical purposes.

cosmic rays particles from space, mostly fast-moving protons (p.155), and the particles they produce in the upper atmosphere (p.31).

dosimetry (*n*) the study of measurement of levels of radioactivity (p.158).

ionizing radiation anything which causes ionization (p.139) in any matter through which it passes, in particular α- (p.158), β- (p.159) and γ- (p.160) particles.

curie (*n*) a unit (p.8) of radioactivity (p.158). A radioactive material which has an activity of one curie is giving off 3.7 x 10^{10} particles per second. One curie = 3.7 x 10^{10} becquerel (↓). **Ci** (*abbr*).

becquerel (*n*) a unit (p.8) of radioactivity (p.158). A radioactive material which has an activity of one becquerel is giving off one particle per second. One becquerel = 2.7 x 10^{-11} curie (↑). **Bq** (*abbr*).

gray (*n*) a measure of the energy released in an object by the ionizing radiation (↑) falling on it. One gray is an energy of one joule (p.17) in each kilogram of the object. **Gy** (*abbr*).

röntgen (*n*) a unit (p.8) which measures the amount of ionization (p.139) caused by ionizing radiation (↑). One röntgen is a level of ionization which releases 2.58 x 10^{-4} coulomb (p.95) of charge (p.95) in every kilogram of air. **R** (*abbr*).

sievert (*n*) a unit (p.8) which measures the amount of damage done to living materials by ionizing radiation (↑). The damage in sievert is equal to the energy released in gray (↑), multiplied by a number which depends on the type of ionizing radiation. This number is about 1 for γ-particles (p.160) and β-particles (p.159), and about 20 for α-particles (p.158). **Sv** (*abbr*).

medical effects of ionizing radiation the ionization (p.139) produced by radioactive (p.158) materials can kill living materials, but it may also change them so that the material lives but produces diseases such as cancer and leukaemia.

film badge a way of measuring the amount of ionizing radiation (↑) falling on a person. It is made of a small piece of photographic material, covered so that no light can fall on it, but it will be changed by any ionizing radiation. The badge is examined regularly to provide a warning of dangerously high levels of ionizing radiation.

curie, becquerel

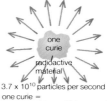

3.7 x 10^{10} particles per second
one curie =
        3.7 x 10^{10} becquerel

gray

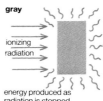

ionizing
radiation

energy produced as
radiation is stopped
one gray = one joule
of energy in each
kilogram of material

röntgen

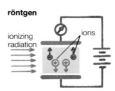

ionizing
radiation   ions

one röntgen = 2.58 x 10^{-4}
coulomb of charge produced
in each kilogram of material

film badge

film   plastic case

window lets through
radiation, but not light

induced fission

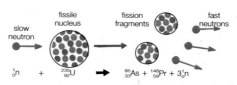

slow neutron

fissile nucleus

fission fragments

fast neutrons

$${}^{1}_{0}n + {}^{235}_{92}U \rightarrow {}^{85}_{33}As + {}^{148}_{59}Pr + 3{}^{1}_{0}n$$

fission (*n*) the splitting of a large nucleus (p.139) into two smaller nuclei, which are usually about equal in size. Since lighter nuclei have relatively fewer neutrons (p.155), some neutrons will also be given off, usually two or three. A particular nuclide (p.155) will not always produce the same pieces, nor will it always produce the same number of neutrons. Since the binding energy per nucleon (p.155) is less in lighter nuclei, energy is also released, mostly in the form of kinetic energy (p.18) in the neutrons. **fissile** (*adj*), **fission** (*v*).

fission fragment either one of the nuclei (p.139) produced in a fission (↑).

induced fission fission (↑) which takes place after a nucleus (p.139) has been hit by a slow-moving neutron (p.155).

chain reaction the state of a system which will continue to operate on its own, often at an accelerating (p.12) rate, once it has been set in motion. In particular, a system containing fissile (↑) material, where each neutron (p.155) which produces an induced fission (↑) releases several more neutrons, which themselves produce further fission, with the release of more neutrons, so that the number of fissions per second increases, as does the amount of energy produced.

chain reaction

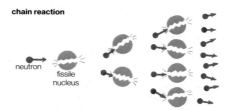

neutron

fissile nucleus

critical (*adj*) of fissile (p.165) material which is in a
state where it is just able to support a chain
reaction (p.165).

critical mass the smallest amount of fissile (p.165)
material of a given type needed to become
critical (↑). If less than this mass is present, the
surface area will be too large in relation to the
volume (p.55), and too many neutrons (p.155)
will escape for a chain reaction (p.165) to begin.
For most pure fissile materials, with a suitable
moderator (↓), the critical mass is several
kilograms.

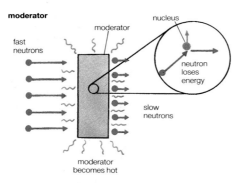

moderator becomes hot

moderator (*n*) a material which slows down
neutrons (p.155) by absorbing (p.242) their
kinetic energy (p.18) in collisions (p.22), without
absorbing too many of the neutrons itself. The
neutrons produced in fission (p.165) are fast
moving and can produce a chain reaction
(p.165) only if they are first slowed down. Light
nuclei (p.139) make the best moderators, as they
gain the most kinetic energy in a collision with a
nucleus. ^{1}H is not used as it absorbs too many
neutrons, so ^{2}H in the form of heavy water (↓) is
used, as is ^{12}C in the form of graphite.

heavy water water in which both the hydrogen
atoms (p.139) are of the isotope (p.156) ^{2}H.

deuterium (*n*) another name for the isotope
(p.156) ^{2}H.

tritium (*n*) another name for the isotope (p.156) ^{3}H.

control rod

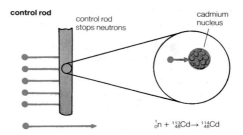

control rod
stops neutrons

cadmium
nucleus

$$^1_0n + \,^{113}_{48}Cd \rightarrow \,^{114}_{48}Cd$$

control rod a rod which can be placed in the
reactor core ($\downarrow$) of a nuclear reactor ($\downarrow$) to control
the chain reaction (p.165). It is made of a material
which absorbs (p.242) neutrons (p.155) without
fission (p.165).

nuclear reactor

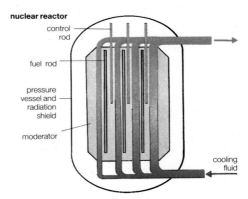

control
rod

fuel rod

pressure
vessel and
radiation
shield

moderator

cooling
fluid

nuclear reactor a machine made to produce a
controlled chain reaction (p.165). Usually such
machines are used to produce heat from the
kinetic energy (p.18) of the neutrons (p.155), but
some small nuclear reactors are used to produce
neutrons for experiments.

reactor core the central part of a nuclear reactor
($\uparrow$). The reactor core holds the fissile (p.165)
material, the moderator ($\uparrow$), and the control rods
($\uparrow$).

meltdown (*n*) the state in which even if the chain reaction (p.165) in a nuclear reactor (p.167) has been stopped by the control rods (p.167), failure to keep the reactor core (p.167) cool results in it melting because of the heat produced in the radioactive (p.158) decay (p.158) of the fission fragments (p.165). In the worst case this might result in radioactive material escaping from the reactor.

atomic bomb a weapon which uses the heat and ionizing radiation (p.164) produced by an uncontrolled chain reaction (p.165).

fast breeder reactor a nuclear reactor (p.167) in which neutrons (p.155) which are not needed for the chain reaction (p.165) are absorbed (p.242) by the isotope (p.156) ^{238}U. After two β-particles (p.159) have been given off, the daughter nuclide (p.158) ^{239}Pu is itself fissile (p.165), and so can be used to power the reactor.

enriched uranium uranium which contains a larger amount of the fissile (p.165) isotope (p.156) ^{235}U than natural uranium. It can be produced by feeding the gas uranium hexafluoride into a centrifuge (p.27), where the slightly different masses of the different isotopes allow them to be separated.

heavy water reactor a nuclear reactor (p.167) in which heavy water (p.166) is used both as a moderator (p.166) and to remove heat from the reactor core (p.167).

gas cooled reactor a nuclear reactor (p.167) in which a gas (usually carbon dioxide) is used to cool the reactor core (p.167), while the moderator (p.166) is usually in the form of solid carbon (graphite).

radioactive waste (1) the fission fragments (p.165) that must be removed from a nuclear reactor (p.167) from time to time to allow new fissile (p.165) material to be used; (2) any parts of the reactor itself which have become radioactive (p.158) after being hit by neutrons (p.155) from the chain reaction (p.165) and are then removed from the reactor core (p.167). Many of these materials contain isotopes (p.156) with long half-lives (p.162), so they must be handled carefully.

fast breeder reactor

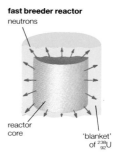

neutrons

reactor core

'blanket' of $^{238}_{92}$U

spark counter

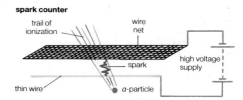

spark counter a detector for ionizing radiation
(p.164) which contains two electrodes (p.113),
one in the form of a fine metal wire, the other a
metal plate or wire net. A high voltage (p.107) is
supplied to these electrodes, so that a spark
(p.100) is produced if any ionization (p.139) is
produced. The sparks can be counted
electronically (p.139) or photographed to record
the path of the ionizing radiation.

Geiger-Müller tube a tube containing a noble gas
(p.140), usually argon, at a low pressure (p.30).
The tube is made of metal and given a negative
charge (p.95) by a power supply of about 450
volt (p.107). The positive side of the supply is
connected to a wire in the centre of the tube.
There is a thin window at one end of the tube to
allow ionizing radiation (p.164) to enter the tube.
The ions (p.139) that are produced by any
particle that enters the tube move towards the
oppositely charged electrode (p.113). As they
go, they hit other gas atoms (p.139), producing
more and more ionization (p.139). When the ions
arrive at the electrodes, a burst of current (p.103)
flows in the tube; these bursts can be counted
electronically (p.139). **GM tube** (*abbr*).

Geiger-Müller tube

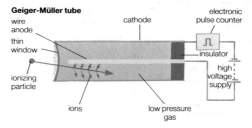

Geiger counter a Geiger-Müller tube (p.169)
together with the circuits (p.104) needed for its
power supply and to detect and count the
ionizing radiation (p.164). The level of
radioactivity (p.158) may be shown on a moving
coil galvanometer (p.117), or each ionizing
(p.139) particle can be made to produce a sound
from a loudspeaker (p.58).

dead time the time when a detector of ionizing
radiation (p.164), particularly a Geiger-Müller
tube (p.169), is still ionized (p.139) from
detecting one particle, and so is not able to
detect a second particle.

cloud chamber

ring of cloth soaked in alcohol

transparent window

β-particle track

α-particle tracks

lamp

dry ice (solid CO$_2$)

metal base painted black

base

cloud chamber an instrument for showing the
paths of particles of ionizing radiation (p.164). It
contains a supersaturated vapour (p.198), which
condenses (p.193) on the ions (p.139) left by an
ionizing (p.139) particle. A simple form of the
cloud chamber contains supersaturated alcohol
vapour, cooled by solid carbon dioxide (dry ice).
As the material in the cloud chamber is a gas,
and so has a low density (p.28), only strongly
ionizing particles such as α-particles (p.158) can
be seen clearly.

bubble chamber

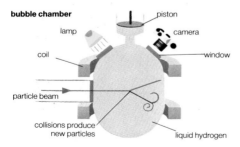

lamp

piston

camera

coil

window

particle beam

collisions produce new particles

liquid hydrogen

bubble chamber an instrument for showing the paths of particles of ionizing radiation (p.164). It contains a superheated liquid (p.198), which boils first along the ions (p.139) left by an ionizing (p.139) particle, so a path of bubbles (p.223) is produced and can be photographed. If the chamber is in a magnetic field (p.92), the paths will be curved, so the momentum (p.21) of the particle can be measured if its charge (p.95) is known. The bubble chamber is able to detect much less strongly ionizing particles than a cloud chamber (↑) because of the greater density (p.28) of the material inside it. Often liquid hydrogen is used in a bubble chamber, so that if the ionizing particle hits a nucleus (p.139), it will be sure to hit a proton (p.155) rather than a neutron (p.155).

photographic radiation detection photographic film behaves in the same way when hit by ionizing radiation (p.164) as it does when hit by light. If the film is covered with a material which allows through radiation but not light, the amount of radiation can be measured.

radiation as a source of heat the ionizing radiation (p.164) given off in radioactive (p.158) decays (p.158) carries a large amount of kinetic energy (p.18). If the particles are stopped, that energy will be changed to heat energy (p.18) in the material that stops the radiation. This can be used as a small energy source, for heating or producing electrical energy (p.111) from a thermocouple (p.105).

radioactive tracer a radioactive (p.158) isotope (p.156) which is placed in a system and then followed through the system using a detector. The isotope will behave in the same way as a non-radioactive isotope of the same element (p.139). The radioactive tracer shows how the system handles that material.

radioactive tracer

clock

water with radioactive isotope as tracer

Geiger counters

radiocarbon dating a way of measuring the age of any material that was once alive. All living material takes up carbon which has come from the atmosphere (p.31). In the upper layers of the atmosphere, cosmic rays (p.163) produce a fixed amount of the isotope ^{14}C, which is radioactive (p.148) with a half-life (p.162) of about 5700 years. When the living material dies, it no longer takes up carbon, so the amount of ^{14}C compared to the amount of non-radioactive ^{12}C decreases. By measuring the amount of ^{14}C, the age of the material can be found.

dating of rocks pieces of rock can have their age found in a way similar to radiocarbon dating (↑), but one which uses isotopes (p.156) of the elements (p.139) strontium or potassium, which have much longer half-lives (p.162).

scintillation counter a detector of ionizing radiation (p.164) which works from the light given off when certain materials are hit by ionizing radiation. The light can either be viewed directly or be measured electronically (p.139) using a photomultiplier (p.149). Zinc sulphide and sodium iodide as well as some plastics make good scintillation counters.

scintillate (*v*) to give off light when hit by ionizing radiation (p.164).

solid state radiation detector a reverse biased (p.134) pn junction (p.134) used to detect ionizing radiation (p.164). When the radiation hits the junction, electrons (p.139) and holes (p.133) will be produced in the depletion layer (p.134), and will move to opposite sides of the junction, causing a burst of current (p.103).

radiocarbon dating

cosmic rays

carbon 14 formed in atmosphere and absorbed by tree

^{14}C

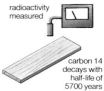

radioactivity measured

carbon 14 decays with half-life of 5700 years

scintillation counter

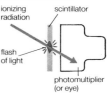

ionizing radiation

scintillator

flash of light

photomultiplier (or eye)

solid state radiation detector

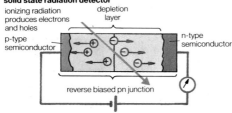

ionizing radiation produces electrons and holes

depletion layer

p-type semiconductor

n-type semiconductor

reverse biased pn junction

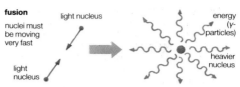

fusion

nuclei must be moving very fast

light nucleus

light nucleus

energy (γ-particles)

heavier nucleus

nuclear fusion (*n*) the coming together of two light nuclei (p.139) to form a heavier nucleus. Since the binding energy per nucleon (p.155) usually increases with atomic number (p.155) for light nuclei, energy may be released, but as both nuclei will be positively charged (p.95), a large amount of energy will be needed to bring the nuclei together first. This can be done by heating the material to a very high temperature. At such temperatures, the material is in a plasma (↓) state.

torus (*n*) a ring-shaped container.

torus

tokamak

vacuum vessel

transformer core

coils

plasma

tokamak (*n*) a torus (↑) in which a plasma (↓) is held by magnetic fields (p.92) from coils (p.115) around the torus and currents (p.103) flowing through the plasma. The current through the plasma, and other supplies of energy, heat the plasma. It is hoped that it will be possible to produce controlled nuclear fusion (↑) in this way.

hydrogen bomb a weapon which uses the energy from the nuclear fusion (↑) of isotopes (p.156) of the element (p.139) hydrogen. The fusion is set off by a small fission explosion. **H-bomb** (*abbr*).

plasma (*n*) the state (p.192) of matter at very high temperature, when the collisions (p.22) between atoms (p.139) are fast enough for the material to be ionized (p.139). A plasma conducts (p.96) electricity, and can be controlled by magnetic fields (p.92).

sub-nuclear particle any particle which is smaller than a nucleus (p.139). Such particles are all thought to be either elementary particles (↓) or made up of quarks (p.176).

elementary particle a particle which is not made up from any smaller particles and so is one of the basic building blocks of matter.

fundamental particle = elementary particle (↑).

lepton

charged particles		neutral particles	
● e^- electron	● e^+ positron	● ν_e electron neutrino	○ $\overline{\nu}_e$ electron antineutrino
● μ^- muons	● μ^+	● ν_μ muon neutrinos	○ $\overline{\nu}_\mu$
● τ^- tau leptons	● τ^+	● ν_τ tau neutrinos	○ $\overline{\nu}_\tau$
? heavier families may still be discovered ?			

lepton (*n*) any fermion (p.151) which does not feel strong nuclear force (p.177).

hadron (*n*) any particle which feels strong nuclear force (p.177).

muon (*n*) a lepton (↑) which has all the same properties as an electron (p.139), except that it has a mass about 200 times that of an electron, and has a half-life (p.162) of about 2×10^{-6}s, turning into an electron and two neutrinos (p.161). A photon (p.148) may also be produced. Also known as **mu-meson**.

mu-meson (*n*) = muon (↑).

meson (*n*) any hadron (↑) which is also a boson (p.151).

muon

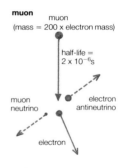

muon
(mass = 200 x electron mass)

half-life = 2×10^{-6}s

muon neutrino

electron antineutrino

electron

meson

positive mesons	neutral mesons	negative mesons	name
● π^+	● π^0	● π^-	pions
● K^+	● K^0 ● $\overline{K}^0$	● K^-	kaons (strange)
	● η^0		eta
● ρ^+	● ρ^0	● ρ^-	rho
	● ω^0		omega
	● η'		eta prime
many heavier meson states are known, but all are very short lived			

increasing mass

pion

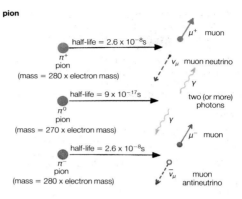

pion (*n*) any member of the lightest family of
mesons (↑), all having a mass of about 280 times
the mass of an electron (p.139). There are
positive and negative pions which usually decay
(p.158) to a muon (↑) and a muon neutrino
(p.161), and a neutral (p.95) pion which usually
decays to two high-energy photons (p.148). Also
known as **pi-meson**.

pi-meson (*n*) = pion (↑).

baryon (*n*) any hadron (↑) which is also a fermion
(p.151). The lightest baryons are the proton
(p.155) and neutron (p.155).

baryon

increasing
mass

baryons			antibaryons			name
positive	neutral	negative	negative	neutral	positive	
● p			● p̄			proton
	● n			● n̄		neutron
	● Λ⁰			● Λ̄⁰		lambda
● Σ⁺	● Σ⁰	● Σ⁻	● Σ̄⁻	● Σ̄⁰	● Σ̄⁺	sigma
Δ⁺⁺ Δ⁺	● Δ⁰	● Δ⁻	● Δ̄⁻⁻ ● Δ̄⁻	● Δ̄⁰	● Δ̄⁺	delta
	● Ξ⁰	● Ξ⁻		● Ξ̄⁰	● Ξ̄⁺	xi
many heavier baryon states are known, but most are very short lived						

baryon number a quantum number (p.151) that is
1 for all baryons (p.175) and −1 for their
antiparticles (p.151). In any decay (p.158) or
collision (p.22) between particles, the baryon
number remains the same, though it is thought
that protons (p.155) may decay to mesons
(p.174) and leptons (p.174). If they do, the
half-life (p.162) is at least 10^{30} years, much
longer than the age of the universe.

strangeness (*n*) a property of some hadrons
(p.174). Decays (p.158) in which the strangeness
changes have long half-lives (p.162), so the
lightest strange particles have unexpectedly long
half-lives. **strange** (*adj*).

charm (*n*) a property of some hadrons (p.174).
Decays (p.158) in which the total charm changes
have long half-lives (p.162), so the lightest
charmed particles have unexpectedly long half-
lives. **charmed** (*adj*).

quark (*n*) a type of sub-nuclear particle (p.174)
thought to be an elementary particle (p.174),
from which all hadrons (p.174) are made up.
Baryons (p.175) are made up of three quarks,
and mesons (p.174) of a quark and an antiquark.
The quarks are called *up*, *down*, *strange*,
charmed, *top* and *bottom*. Protons (p.155) and
neutrons (p.155) are made of up and down
quarks. The up quark has a positive charge
(p.95), two thirds of that on a proton, while the
down quark has a negative charge, one third of
that on an electron (p.139). Protons are made
from two up quarks and one down quark.
Neutrons are made of two down quarks and one
up quark.

gluon (*n*) the particle that carries the strong
nuclear force (↓) and holds quarks (p.176)
together in hadrons (p.174).

W and Z bosons the particles which carry the
weak nuclear force (p.14). They have masses of
about 80 and 90 times the mass of a proton
(p.155). The W-boson is charged (p.95), positive
or negative, while the Z-boson is neutral (p.95).

weak intermediate vector bosons = W and Z
bosons (↑).

weak vector bosons = W and Z bosons (↑).

quark

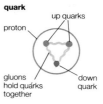

proton

up quarks

gluons
hold quarks
together

down
quark

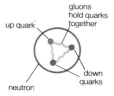

up quark

gluons
hold quarks
together

down
quarks

neutron

particle physics the study of physics (p.238) where small numbers of particles carry high energies, usually at least 10^8 electronvolt (p.149) per particle. The higher the energy carried by a particle the smaller its de Broglie wavelength (p.152), so the smaller the objects that can be studied. Also if a single particle gives up a large amount of energy in a collision (p.22), this energy can be turned into mass (*see equivalence of mass and energy* (p.18)). This makes new particles, which could not be produced in any other way. Also known as **elementary particle physics** or **high energy physics**.
elementary particle physics = particle physics (↑).
high energy physics = particle physics (↑).

four forces of nature

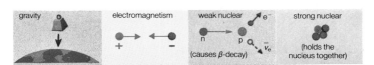

gravity · electromagnetism · weak nuclear e^- · strong nuclear
$+$ $-$ · n p $\bar{v_e}$ (causes β-decay) · (holds the nucleus together)

four forces of nature it is thought that all of physics (p.238) can be explained using just four types of force: gravity (p.23); electromagnetic (p.115) force; strong nuclear force (↓); and weak nuclear force (p.178). Outside the nucleus (p.139) only gravity and electromagnetism are important; e.g. the contact force (p.14) between two objects touching each other is a result of the electromagnetic force.

strong nuclear force the force which holds protons (p.155) and neutrons (p.155) together in a nucleus (p.139). At short distances it is stronger than the electromagnetic force (p.14), so nuclei do not fall apart from the repulsion (p.239) between protons. The strong nuclear force is a short range force, so the largest nuclei are less stable (p.236), and are likely to decay (p.158), either by giving off an α-particle (p.158) or by spontaneous fission (p.162). The strong nuclear force is explained by hadrons (p.174) being made up of quarks (↑) which have a property called colour (p.178), although the hadron as a whole has no colour.

weak nuclear force the force which causes β-
particle (p.159) decay (p.158), in which neutrons
(p.155) and protons (p.155) can turn into one
another, giving off an electron (p.139) or positron
(p.151), along with a neutrino (p.161) or
antineutrino (p.161). This force is also involved in
nuclear fusion (p.173) in stars.

electroweak theory

proton made from
three quarks

proton

proton

photon

Z boson (like
a photon, but
with mass)

electron

neutrino

force between electron and
proton caused by photon

force between neutrino and
proton caused by Z boson

electroweak theory a theory (p.238) which states
that the electromagnetic (p.115) force and the
weak nuclear force (↑) are two parts of the same
force, called the *electroweak force*, but they
appear different at all but the highest energies.
The theory led to the discovery of the W and Z
bosons (p.176). Also known as the **Weinberg-
Salam theory**.
Weinberg-Salam theory = electroweak theory (↑).
grand unified theory a theory (p.238) in which the
electroweak (↑) force and the strong nuclear
force (p.177) become one at high energies. Such
theories state that protons (p.155) will decay
(p.158) with a very long half-life (p.162).
Experiments looking for the decay of protons
have shown that only some of these theories are
possible. **G.U.T.** (*abbr*).
colour[2] (*n*) a property of quarks (p.176) and gluons
(p.176). Quarks come in one of three colours,
gluons in one of eight colours, but any hadron
(p.174) is **colour neutral**, having no colour of its
own; but the colour within hadrons causes the
strong nuclear force (p.177). Colour in the high
energy physics (p.177) sense has nothing to do
with colour as in the wavelength (p.43) of visible
(p.88) light.

particle accelerator a machine for accelerating (p.12) charged (p.95) particles to high energies. In this way they can be used to study matter at small distances, or their energy can be used to make particles of higher mass (p.8) (*see equivalence of mass and energy* (p.18)). Particle accelerators use electric fields (p.97) to accelerate the particles. Magnetic fields (p.92) cannot be used to increase the energy of the particle, as the magnetic force on a moving charged particle is always at right angles to the direction in which the particle is moving, so it can do no work (p.17). Magnetic fields are used to change the paths of particles, e.g. to keep them moving in circles, or to form them into a narrow beam.

van de Graaff accelerator a particle accelerator (↑) which uses a van de Graaff generator (p.100) to charge (p.95) an electrode (p.113) to a high electrical potential (p.18). Particles with the same charge as this electrode then accelerate (p.12) away, gaining kinetic energy (p.18). The largest energy that can be given to a particle by this type of particle accelerator is controlled by the insulation (p.97) of the electrode. The largest potential that can be reached is a few million volt (p.107).

van de Graaff accelerator

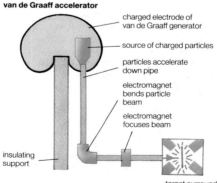

charged electrode of van de Graaff generator

source of charged particles

particles accelerate down pipe

electromagnet bends particle beam

electromagnet focuses beam

insulating support

target surrounded by particle detectors

cyclotron

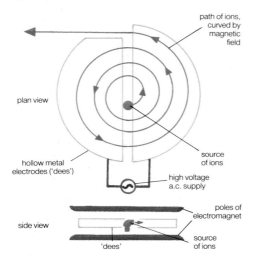

path of ions, curved by magnetic field

plan view

hollow metal electrodes ('dees')

source of ions

high voltage a.c. supply

poles of electromagnet

side view

'dees'

source of ions

cyclotron (*n*) a particle accelerator (p.179) in which a magnetic field (p.92) makes charged (p.95) particles move in circular paths inside hollow D-shaped electrodes (p.113). An alternating voltage (p.125) is connected to these electrodes, and the frequency (p.36) of this voltage is chosen so that each time a particle passes from one electrode to the other, the electric field (p.97) between them is in the right direction to accelerate (p.12) the particle. This increases the radius of the path in which the particle is moving, until it leaves the machine, having been accelerated many times. If the mass of the particle does not change, the time taken to complete one circle in the machine will not depend on how quickly a particle is moving. The largest energy that can be given to a particle is controlled by the increase in mass when the particle reaches relativistic (p.34) speeds.

dee (*n*) the hollow D-shaped electrode (p.113) in a cyclotron (↑).

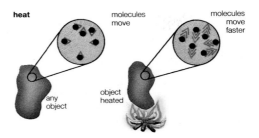

heat

molecules move

molecules move faster

any object

object heated

heat (*n*) energy which is held in the form of random (p.235) motions of the atoms (p.139) or molecules (p.188) from which a body is made. This energy flows from one body to another if there is a difference in temperature (↓). **heat** (*v*).

thermal (*adj*) having to do with heat (↑).

temperature (*n*) a measure of how hot or cold a thing is. This depends not only on how much heat energy (p.18) a body contains, but also on the mass of the body and on the material from which it is made. If the temperature of a particular object is increased, it will then contain more heat energy.

zeroth law of thermodynamics when two objects are placed together, so heat (↑) can flow from one object to another, the heat will flow from the higher temperature (↑) body to the lower temperature body. E.g. when a flame is placed in contact with a block of warm metal, because the flame is at a higher temperature, the heat flows into the metal even though the metal may already contain more heat energy (p.18) than the flame.

zeroth law of thermodynamics

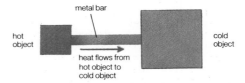

metal bar

hot object

cold object

heat flows from hot object to cold object

thermometer (*n*) an instrument for measuring temperature (p.181). Many different types of thermometer have been made. The type used in a particular case depends on the temperature to be measured, and on whether it is more important to measure the temperature quickly, or to have an accurate (p.240) result. The thermometer itself may heat or cool the system that is being measured if that system has a small heat capacity (p.185).

liquid in glass thermometer a thermometer (↑) which uses the expansion (p.214) of a liquid which is stored in a space, called the *bulb*, formed in the bottom of a glass tube called the *stem* of the thermometer. Because liquids generally expand more than solids when heated, the liquid rises further up the stem as the temperature rises. A scale on the stem allows the temperature to be measured. Mercury is often used as the liquid in a thermometer, but for measuring temperatures below the freezing point (p.192) of mercury, other liquids may be used. A liquid in glass thermometer will be more sensitive (p.240) if it has a large bulb and a thin bore (↓) to the stem. A thermometer like this has the disadvantage that it will have to be very long if it is to cover a wide range of temperatures.

stem (*n*) the glass tube in a liquid in glass thermometer (↑).

bore (*n*) (1) a hole down the middle of a tube; (2) the size of this hole.

liquid in glass thermometer

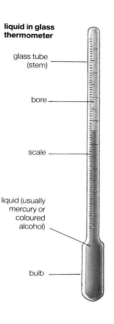

- glass tube (stem)
- bore
- scale
- liquid (usually mercury or coloured alcohol)
- bulb

platinum resistance thermometer

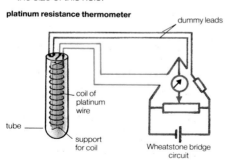

- dummy leads
- coil of platinum wire
- tube
- support for coil
- Wheatstone bridge circuit

platinum resistance thermometer a
thermometer (↑) which uses the change in
resistance (p.108) with temperature (p.181) of a
coil (p.115) of platinum wire. Platinum is chosen
as it is not easily attacked in chemical reactions
(p.236), and has a high melting point (p.191), so
it can be used where a liquid in glass
thermometer (↑) could not. The resistance is
measured by a Wheatstone bridge (p.112) which
also includes a pair of wires called *dummy leads*
which run with the wires connecting the platinum
wire to the Wheatstone bridge. In this way the
results do not vary with changes in the resistance
of the wires connecting (p.104) the platinum wire
to the resistance measuring circuit (p.104).

constant volume gas thermometer

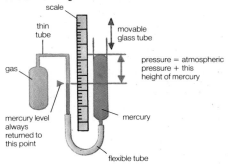

scale

thin
tube

movable
glass tube

gas

pressure = atmospheric
pressure + this
height of mercury

mercury level
always
returned to
this point

mercury

flexible tube

constant volume gas thermometer a thermometer (↑) which measures the change in the
pressure (p.30) of a fixed mass of gas contained
in a fixed volume. Such a thermometer can give
very accurate (p.240) readings of temperature
(p.181), since the behaviour of an ideal gas
(p.199) is directly linked to the thermodynamic
temperature scale (p.184). Such measurements
are difficult to make and take time.

temperature scale a way of giving numbers to
temperatures (p.181), so that objects at different
temperatures will be given different numbers.
Usually higher temperatures are given higher
numbers.

thermodynamic temperature scale

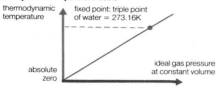

thermodynamic temperature scale a
temperature scale (p.183) which is based on the
second law of thermodynamics (p.204). The
kinetic theory (p.188) of gases shows that this
temperature scale is also the correct one to use
when describing the behaviour of an ideal gas
(p.199). It has absolute zero (p.207) as the zero
of temperature, and equal increases in temperature cause the pressure (p.30) of a fixed mass of
an ideal gas held in a fixed volume to increase by
equal amounts. The second fixed point (↓) is the
triple point (p.197) of water, which is given the
temperature of 273.16 kelvin (↓). Also known as
absolute temperature scale.

absolute temperature scale = thermodynamic
temperature scale (↑).

absolute temperature temperature (p.181)
measured on the thermodynamic temperature
scale (↑).

kelvin (*n*) the unit (p.8) of temperature (p.181) in
the thermodynamic temperature scale (↑). The
triple point (p.197) of water is 273.16 kelvin, the
freezing and boiling points of water are 273.15
kelvin and 373.15 kelvin, both at a pressure
(p.30) of 1.01×10^5 pascal (p.30). **K** (*abbr*).

Celsius temperature scale a temperature scale
(p.183) in which the lower fixed point (↓) is the
freezing point (p.192) of pure water at atmospheric pressure (p.31): this is 0°C. The upper
fixed point is the boiling point (p.192) of pure
water at atmospheric pressure; this is 100°C.

fixed point a point on a temperature scale (p.183)
which is given a particular temperature (p.181),
usually one which can easily be held accurately,
e.g. a boiling point (p.192). Any temperature
scale must have at least two fixed points.

Celsius temperature scale

specific heat capacity

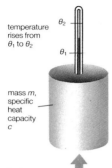

temperature rises from θ_1 to θ_2

θ_2

θ_1

mass m, specific heat capacity c

heat energy supplied = $mc(\theta_2 - \theta_1)$

heat capacity the amount of heat energy (p.18) needed to raise the temperature (p.181) of a given object by a given amount, usually one kelvin (↑). The heat capacity of an object depends both on the mass of the object and on the material from which it is made.

specific heat capacity the heat capacity (↑) of an object divided by its mass. The specific heat capacity of a material does not depend on how much of the material there is, and it changes little with temperature (p.181). Thus the amount of heat energy (p.18) needed to increase the temperature of an object of mass m from a temperature θ_1 to a higher temperature θ_2 is $mc(\theta_2 - \theta_1)$, where c is the specific heat capacity of the material from which the object is made. **s.h.c.** (*abbr*).

molar heat capacity the heat capacity (↑) of an object divided by the number of moles (p.237) of material present. Like specific heat capacity (↑) this depends only on what the material is and not on how much of it there is.

Dulong and Petit's law an empirical (p.238) law which states that at high enough temperatures (p.181) the molar heat capacity (↑) of any solid will tend to the value $3R$, where R is the molar gas constant (p.200). This is the result of the principle of equipartition of energy (p.186) used for the vibration (p.242) of atoms (p.139) in a solid, there being kinetic energy (p.18) and potential energy (p.17) from motion in each of three directions at 90° to one another, a total of six degrees of freedom (p.186).

Dulong and Petit's law

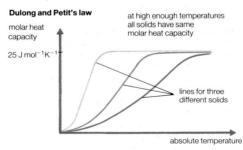

molar heat capacity

at high enough temperatures all solids have same molar heat capacity

$25 \text{ J mol}^{-1}\text{K}^{-1}$

lines for three different solids

absolute temperature

degree of freedom one of the separate ways in which a molecule (p.188) can have energy. A molecule made up of a single atom (p.139) in a gas will have three degrees of freedom: kinetic energy (p.18) from motion in three directions at 90° to one another. A molecule made of two atoms in a line can also turn, but quantum mechanics (p.150) leads to the result that thermal (p.181) motion cannot produce turning about the line joining the two atoms together, so here there are five degrees of freedom.

principle of equipartition of energy the idea that a system will have an average thermal energy (p.18) of $kT/2$ per molecule (p.188) for each degree of freedom (↑), where k is the Boltzmann constant (p.191), and T is the thermodynamic temperature (p.181) of the system.

electrical measurement of specific heat capacity the simplest way to measure the specific heat capacity (p.185) of a material is to heat a piece of that material electrically. The amount of electrical energy (p.111) supplied is measured from the power (p.19) of the heater and the time for which the heater operates. The temperature (p.181) rise produced is measured, and if the mass of the material is known, the specific heat capacity can be found. In fact not all the heat from the heater goes into heating the material. The heat lost can be reduced with good thermal insulation (p.210), or a cooling correction (↓) can be made.

electrical measurement of specific heat capacity

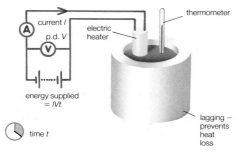

degree of freedom

(1)
a single atom in a gas has three degrees of freedom

(2)
a linear molecule in a gas has five degrees of freedom

(3)
a non-linear molecule in a gas has six degrees of freedom

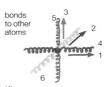

(4)
an atom in a solid has six degrees of freedom

measurement of specific heat capacity by method of mixtures

mass m_1
specific heat capacity c_1
temperature θ_1

thermometer

calorimeter or lagged container

mass m_2
specific heat capacity c_2
temperature θ_2

new temperature θ_3

liquids mixed and stirred

$$m_1 c_1 (\theta_1 - \theta_3) = m_2 c_2 (\theta_3 - \theta_2)$$

measurement of specific heat capacity by method of mixtures a way of measuring the specific heat capacity (p.185) of a material by mixing it or placing it in thermal contact (p.210) with a known mass of material of known specific heat capacity at a different temperature (p.181). The warmer material will cool down, giving heat energy (p.18) to the cooler material, which will heat up. If the temperature changes are measured and no heat is lost, the specific heat capacity of one of the materials can be found.

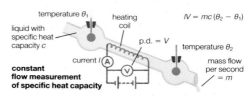

temperature θ_1

heating coil

$IV = mc(\theta_2 - \theta_1)$

liquid with specific heat capacity c

p.d. = V

temperature θ_2

current I

mass flow per second = m

constant flow measurement of specific heat capacity

constant flow measurement of specific heat capacity a way of measuring the specific heat capacity (p.185) of a liquid, in which the liquid flows steadily over an electric heater. The heat energy (p.18) given to the liquid each second can be found from the power (p.19) of the heater. The specific heat capacity can then be found if the mass per second flowing over the heater and the temperature (p.181) rise produced are measured.

calorimeter (n) a container used for holding a material whose specific heat capacity (p.185) is to be measured. The container is usually made of a good conductor (p.96) of heat, so that it will all reach the same temperature.

cooling correction a calculation or experiment to find the difference between the temperature (p.181) measured in an experiment to find a specific heat capacity (p.185), and the temperature that would have been reached if no heat (p.181) had been lost to the surroundings of the experiment. The amount of heat loss can be found by measuring how quickly the materials used in the experiment cool when no heat is being supplied.

kinetic theory that part of physics (p.238) which explains the way matter behaves, using the motion of particles called molecules (↓). The molecules behave differently in solids, liquids and gases, but in each case they move more as the temperature (p.181) increases.

molecule (*n*) one or more atoms (p.139) held together by covalent bonds (p.221) to form an object which will not be broken up by thermal (p.181) vibrations (p.242). For the purposes of kinetic theory (↑) each molecule can be considered as a single object, however many atoms it may contain.

kinetic theory of solids in a solid the molecules (↑) from which the solid are made each have their own fixed positions. It is for this reason that a solid cannot easily change its shape. The molecules are not fixed tightly to these positions, but vibrate (p.242) about them. The amount of vibration depends on the temperature (p.181) of the solid. The molecules in a solid are packed closely together, which means that there is little empty space.

kinetic theory of gases in a gas the molecules (↑) are far apart. They move at random (p.235), and as they are far apart from each other the intermolecular forces (p.218) are weak and a gas will expand to fill the whole of the space in which it is contained. The pressure (p.30) a gas produces on the walls of its container is caused by the molecules of the gas hitting the walls. The pressure depends on the number of molecules per second hitting a given area of the wall and on the average speed of the molecules. Thus the pressure is increased if the volume (p.55) of the container is reduced, or if the speed of the molecules is increased by heating the gas. The collisions (p.22) between the molecules of the gas and the container walls are elastic (p.224), otherwise the gas molecules would soon lose all their kinetic energy (p.18). If the size of the container is reduced, the molecules of the gas will tend to come off the moving walls with an increased speed, so the gas temperature (p.181) will go up.

kinetic theory of solids

each molecule vibrates about a fixed position

solid

kinetic theory of gases

molecules far apart, move at random, do not often hit other molecules

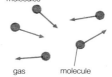

gas   molecule

kinetic theory of liquids
molecules closely spaced, move at random, often hit other molecules

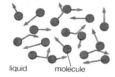

liquid   molecule

kinetic theory of liquids in a liquid the molecules (↑) are packed together nearly as closely as they are in a solid. This is why the density (p.28) of a material in its liquid and solid states is nearly the same. But in a liquid the molecules do not have fixed positions; they are free to move at random (p.235). This is why a liquid will take up the shape of its container. As the molecules are close together, the intermolecular forces (p.218) are quite strong, so a liquid will not expand (p.214) to fill the whole of a container, but will lie at the bottom of the container.

kinetic theory of phase changes when a solid is heated, the vibration (p.242) of the molecules (↑) will increase to the point where the vibrational energy (p.17) is enough for the molecules to break free of their fixed positions, and a liquid will be formed. In a liquid some of the molecules that are moving quickly and are near the surface may escape into the space above the liquid; this is evaporation (p.192). As only the fastest molecules escape, the liquid left behind will be cooler (*see cooling by evaporation* (p.193)). A liquid boils (p.192) when bubbles of vapour (p.195) form within the liquid.

mean free path the average distance that a molecule (↑) will travel before it hits another molecule. In a liquid this distance is about the same as the size of a molecule, but in a gas it is much larger than this. The mean free path controls the ability of a molecule to carry energy and momentum (p.21) from one part of a fluid (p.30) to another. This is related to the thermal conductivity (p.210) and viscosity (p.32) of the fluid. In a gas containing n molecules per unit volume, each with a cross sectional area (p.233) σ, the mean free path is $1/(2^{1/2}n\pi\sigma^2)$.

mean free path

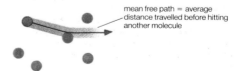

mean free path = average distance travelled before hitting another molecule

diffusion (*n*) the spreading of one material into another even when they are not mixed by any motion of the material as a whole. If a small amount of one gas is released into another gas, it will spread much more slowly than it would if it were released into a vacuum (p.242), because its molecules (p.188) will collide (p.22) with the molecules of the other gas. The rate at which a gas diffuses into another depends on the speed at which its molecules are moving; the faster they move the more rapid the diffusion. That gases diffuse at different speeds can be seen in an experiment in which gases are allowed to diffuse through a porous (p.242) pot. Gases with light molecules, e.g. hydrogen, will diffuse into the pot more quickly than the air diffuses out, so the pressure in the pot will rise. Gases with heavier molecules, e.g. carbon dioxide, will diffuse into the pot more slowly than the air diffuses out, so the pressure in the pot will fall (*see mean speed of molecules in a gas* (↓)). **diffuse** (*v*).

mean speed of molecules in a gas the root mean square (p.127) speed of molecules (p.188) in an ideal gas can be found from the force they produce when they hit the wall of the container. The result is $pV = Nm(c_{rms})^2/3$, where p is the pressure (p.30), V is the volume (p.55), N is the number of molecules in the gas, m is the mass of a molecule of the gas, and c_{rms} is the root mean square speed of the molecules. This speed is a little more than the speed of sound (p.55) in the gas; this is as would be expected, for the sound travels through the gas by way of the molecules. A gas like hydrogen, which has much lighter molecules, will have faster moving molecules for the same pressure, so the speed of sound in hydrogen is faster than in air, as is the rate of diffusion (↑).

Dalton's law of partial pressures in any container in which there is a mixture (p.237) of gases, the total pressure (p.30) that the gases will produce on the container can be found by adding up the partial pressures (↓) that each gas on its own would produce.

diffusion

hydrogen diffuses into pot more quickly than air diffuses out

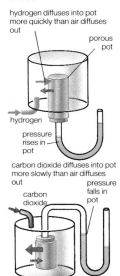

carbon dioxide diffuses into pot more slowly than air diffuses out

Dalton's law of partial pressures

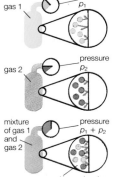

pressure caused by molecules hitting container walls

random walk

each step in a random
direction

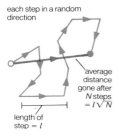

length of
step $= l$

average
distance
gone after
N steps
$= l \sqrt{N}$

oil film experiment

oil drop spreads over surface,
pushing back powder

water coated
with fine powder

tray of water

Brownian motion

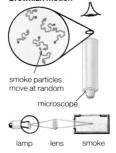

smoke particles
move at random

microscope

lamp   lens   smoke

partial pressure the pressure (p.30) that a single
gas in a mixture (p.237) of gases would produce
if none of the other gases in the mixture were
present. The total pressure in a mixture of gases
can be found by adding the partial pressures of
each gas in the mixture.

Graham's law of diffusion the speed of diffusion
(↑) is inversely proportional (p.235) to the square
root of its density (p.28). This follows from the
link between the speed of molecules (p.188) and
the volume (p.55) of a given mass of gas at a
given temperature (p.181).

random walk the path followed by a single
molecule (p.188) in a gas. The molecule travels a
random (p.235) distance before hitting another
molecule in an elastic collision (p.21) and setting
off in a random direction. If a molecule makes N
steps, each of length l, in random directions, the
average distance of the molecule from its starting
point will then be $l/(N^{1/2})$.

oil film experiment an experiment to find the size
of a molecule (p.188). A bowl of water is covered
with a fine powder and a drop of oil is placed on
the surface. The oil drop spreads out, pushing
back the powder. The area of the oil film
produced can be measured, and if this film is one
molecule thick, the size of a molecule can be
found from the size of the drop. In fact the film is
not this thin, so the experiment only gives the
largest size an oil molecule could be.

Boltzmann's constant a fundamental constant
(p.234), equal to the molar gas constant (p.200)
divided by Avogadro's number (p.237). The
average thermal energy (p.18) of a molecule
(p.188) at an absolute temperature (p.184) T
is $kT/2$ for each degree of freedom (p.186),
where k is Boltzmann's constant.
$k = 1.38 \times 10^{-23}$ J K^{-1}.

Brownian motion the random (p.235) motion of
smoke particles, or other small particles in a gas
or liquid, seen when they are viewed through a
microscope (p.74). The motion is caused by the
collisions (p.22) of the molecules (p.188) in the
gas or liquid with the smoke particles, causing
them to move at random.

phase[2] (*n*) any of the possible arrangements of molecules (p.188) in a material. For any material, there will be liquid and gas phases. There will also be one or more solid phases. For materials where the molecules are made of single atoms (p.139), there will be a plasma (p.173) phase at very high temperatures (p.181). If there is more than one solid phase, these are called *allotropes* (↓).

state (*n*) there are three states of matter: solid, liquid and gas.

melt (*v*) to change from the solid state (↑) to the liquid state. Also known as **fuse**.

fuse[2] (*v*) = melt (↑).

melting point the temperature (p.181) at which the solid and liquid states (↑) of a material can exist together. The melting point varies with pressure (p.30). Also known as **freezing point**. **m.p.** (*abbr*).

freezing point = melting point (↑).

freeze (*v*) to change from the liquid state (↑) to the solid state.

boil (*v*) to change from the liquid state (↑) to the gas state, with the change taking place all through the liquid, so that bubbles (p.223) of gas are formed.

boiling point the temperature (p.181) at which a liquid boils (↑). The boiling point varies with pressure (p.30). At any given pressure the boiling point is the temperature at which the saturated vapour pressure (p.195) of the liquid is equal to the pressure on the liquid.

evaporation (*n*) the action of changing from the liquid state (↑) to the gas state at temperatures (p.181) below boiling point (↑). This is caused by the fastest molecules (p.188) escaping from the surface of the liquid. If the vapour (p.195) formed above the liquid is not allowed to escape, the evaporation will continue until the vapour pressure (p.195) reaches the point at which the molecules from the vapour return to the liquid as often as they leave it. The vapour pressure will then be equal to the saturated vapour pressure (p.195). **evaporate** (*v*).

vaporize (*v*) to change into a gas.

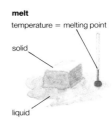

melt
temperature = melting point
solid
liquid

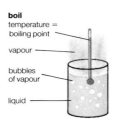

boil
temperature = boiling point
vapour
bubbles of vapour
liquid

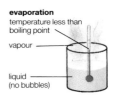

evaporation
temperature less than boiling point
vapour
liquid (no bubbles)

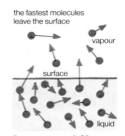

the fastest molecules leave the surface
vapour
surface
liquid
the average speed of the molecules gets less as the fastest molecules leave

cooling by evaporation the drop in temperature (p.181) that is seen when a liquid, particularly a volatile (↓) one, evaporates (↑). This happens because the fastest molecules (p.188) are the ones that have enough energy to escape from the surface of the liquid, so the average speed of the ones left behind will be less, resulting in a drop in temperature.

condense (v) to change from the gas state (↑) to the liquid state.

volatile (adj) evaporating (↑) quickly; having a high saturated vapour pressure (p.195).

allotrope (n) any of the different solid phases (↑) in a material which has more than one phase in the solid state (↑).

allotropy (n) the property of having more than one solid phase (↑).

latent heat the heat energy (p.18) that is needed to change material from one state (↑) to another without changing its temperature (p.181). This energy is used to overcome the interatomic forces (p.218) between the molecules (p.188), but not to increase their kinetic energy (p.18).

allotrope

allotropes of carbon

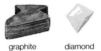

graphite   diamond

latent heat of fusion

solid at melting point   heat required = latent heat of fusion   liquid at melting point

heat breaks the bonds between molecules

molecules fixed in position   molecules free to move

latent heat of fusion the heat energy (p.18) that is needed to change a material from the solid state (↑) to the liquid state, or that is given out when the material changes from the liquid state to the solid state, without causing a change in temperature (p.181). This energy is equal to the energy in the bonds (p.221) that hold the molecules (p.188) in their fixed positions in a solid.

specific latent heat of fusion the amount of heat energy (p.18) needed to take one kilogram of a material in the solid state (↑) at its melting point (↑) into the liquid state at the same temperature (p.181).

latent heat of vaporization

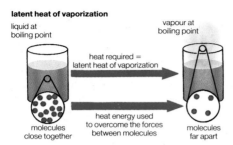

liquid at
boiling point

vapour at
boiling point

heat required =
latent heat of vaporization

molecules
close together

heat energy used
to overcome the forces
between molecules

molecules
far apart

latent heat of vaporization the heat energy
(p.18) needed to change a material from the
liquid state (p.192) to the gas state without
changing its temperature (p.181), or that is given
out when the material changes from the gas
state to the liquid state. It is equal to the energy in
the interatomic forces (p.218) that hold the molecules (p.188) close together in the liquid state.

specific latent heat of vaporization the heat
energy (p.18) needed to take one kilogram of
material from the liquid state (p.192) to the gas
state without changing its temperature (p.181).

electrical measurement of latent heat the latent
heat (p.193) of a material can be measured by
melting (p.192) or boiling (p.192) it with an
electric heater. The energy given to the heater
can be measured, as can the mass of material
melted or boiled. From this the specific latent
heat of fusion (p.193) or the specific latent heat
of vaporization (↑) can be found.

electrical measurement of latent heat

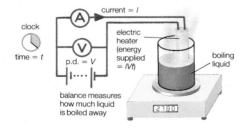

clock

time = t

current = I

electric
heater
(energy
supplied
= IVt)

p.d. = V

boiling
liquid

balance measures
how much liquid
is boiled away

2780

measurement of latent heat by the method of mixtures

solid at known temperature

thermometer

hot liquid

liquid cools, some of the heat is used to melt the solid

liquid stirred to reach even temperature

saturated vapour pressure

pressure of vapour = saturated vapour pressure

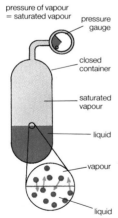

pressure gauge

closed container

saturated vapour

liquid

vapour

liquid

molecules enter and leave the liquid at the same rate

measurement of latent heat by the method of mixtures the specific latent heat of fusion (p.193) or the specific latent heat of vaporization (↑) of a material can be found by mixing (p.237) it with another material which is at a high enough or low enough temperature (p.181) to cause a change in state (p.192) of the first material. The masses of the materials used must be known, as must their starting temperatures and the end temperature of the mixture. Some of the heat energy (p.18) that has gone from one material to the other will be used to produce these temperature changes, so the specific heat capacities (p.185) of both materials must also be known.

vapour (n) the gas state (p.192) of a material when the material is at a temperature (p.181) below its boiling point (p.192); particularly the gas found above the surface of that material in its liquid state.

vapour pressure the partial pressure (p.191) produced by a vapour (↑).

saturated vapour pressure the partial pressure (p.191) of a vapour (↑) when it is in dynamic equilibrium (p.16) with its liquid, or would be if there were any liquid present. The rate at which the liquid evaporates (p.192) is then equal to the rate at which molecules (p.188) from the vapour enter the surface of the liquid. If a liquid is surrounded by its vapour at this pressure, more of the liquid will evaporate only if the temperature (p.181) rises. If the temperature falls, liquid will condense (p.193) until the vapour pressure has fallen to the lower saturated vapour pressure of the lower temperature. The boiling point (p.192) of a liquid at a given pressure is the temperature at which the saturated vapour pressure of the liquid is equal to that pressure. **s.v.p.** (abbr).

saturated vapour a vapour (↑) which has a pressure (p.30) equal to its saturated vapour pressure (↑). If a liquid partly fills a closed container, then the partial pressure (p.191) of the vapour will be equal to the saturated vapour pressure once equilibrium (p.16) has been reached, no matter what other gases are present.

change of boiling point with pressure a liquid
will boil (p.192) at lower temperatures (p.181) if
the pressure is lower, and at higher temperatures
if the pressure is higher. This is because the
boiling point (p.192) of a liquid is the temperature
at which the saturated vapour pressure (p.195)
of the liquid is equal to the pressure (p.30) on the
liquid, and saturated vapour pressure increases
with temperature.

change of melting point with pressure for
materials which contract (p.214) on freezing
(p.192), which most do, an increase in pressure
(p.30) will raise the melting point (p.192). Those
materials which expand (p.214) on freezing,
including water, will tend to melt (p.192) when
they are under greater pressure, as an increase
in pressure lowers their melting point.

**measurement of boiling point from saturated
vapour pressure** the boiling point (p.192) of a
liquid can be found by placing a small amount of
the material in the short arm of a J-shaped glass
tube with some mercury. The other arm of the
tube is left open to the air. The tube is then
heated until the saturated vapour (p.195) in the
closed end of the tube has reached atmospheric
pressure (p.31). At this point the level of the
mercury in the two arms of the tube will be equal.
The temperature (p.181) at which this happens is
the boiling point.

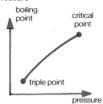

**change of boiling point with
pressure**

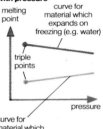

**change of melting point
with pressure**

**measurement of boiling point from saturated vapour
pressure**

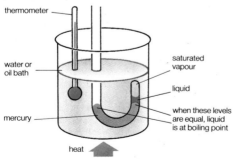

measurement of saturated vapour pressure

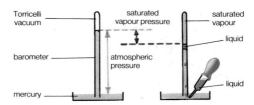

measurement of saturated vapour pressure
the saturated vapour pressure (p.195) of a liquid
can be found by placing some of that liquid into
the Torricelli vacuum (p.31) in a mercury
barometer (p.31). The liquid will evaporate (p.192)
until it is in dynamic equilibrium (p.16) with its
vapour (p.195). The fall in the height of the
mercury in the barometer is equal to the saturated
vapour pressure of the liquid.

sublimation

sublimation (*n*) the action of changing a solid to a
gas without passing through a liquid state (p.192).
This happens very slightly with all materials, but a
great deal with those materials that have triple
points (↓) above atmospheric pressure (p.31).
sublime (*v*).

triple point the one temperature (p.181) and
pressure (p.30) at which the solid, liquid and gas
states (p.192) can all exist together in dynamic
equilibrium (p.16).

phase diagram

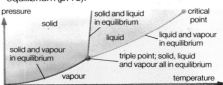

phase diagram a graph of pressure (p.30) against
temperature (p.181) on which three lines are
drawn to show the points where two phases
(p.192) can exist in dynamic equilibrium (p.16).
Two of these lines show the change in freezing
point (p.192) and boiling point (p.192) with
pressure, the third shows the dynamic equilibrium
between solid and vapour (p.195). The three lines
meet at the triple point (↑).

regelation (*n*) the melting (p.192) of ice under a high pressure (p.30). The ice freezes (p.192) again when the pressure is removed.

supercooled liquid a liquid that has been cooled below its freezing point (p.192). Before a solid can form, centres are needed on which the solid can begin to grow. These centres are often small dust particles or faults on the walls of a container. Once the solid has begun to form in a supercooled liquid, it will grow rapidly, giving off heat from the latent heat of fusion (p.193).

superheated liquid a liquid that has been heated above its boiling point (p.192). A large amount of energy is needed to form small bubbles (p.223), and these often form first on faults in the wall of the container. In a smooth container a liquid may be superheated quite a lot before it boils. Once bubbles begin to form in a superheated liquid, they grow very rapidly. This is a violent form of boiling called *bumping*. This can be avoided by placing a small amount of solid material with a rough surface in the container to provide areas where the bubbles can begin to form. Bubbles also form along any trail of ions, e.g. in a bubble chamber (p.171).

supersaturated vapour a vapour (p.195) which has been cooled below the temperature (p.181) at which it would be expected to condense (p.193), i.e. the vapour pressure (p.195) is above the saturated vapour pressure (p.195) for that temperature. Small drops of liquid can form only if there is something around which they can grow, such as a dust particle. The ionized (p.139) particles left in a cloud chamber (p.170) by ionizing radiation (p.164) also act as centres on which drops may form.

condensation nucleus a centre on which a drop of liquid may form when a vapour (p.195) condenses (p.193), on which a bubble (p.223) may form when a liquid boils (p.192), or on which a solid may form when a liquid freezes (p.192). Dust particles, faults on a container wall and trails of ionization (p.139) can all act as condensation nuclei.

regelation

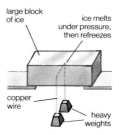

large block of ice

ice melts under pressure, then refreezes

copper wire

heavy weights

Boyle's law

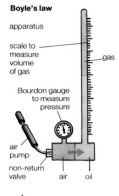

apparatus

scale to measure volume of gas

gas

Bourdon gauge to measure pressure

air pump

non-return valve   air   oil

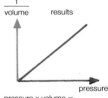

$\dfrac{1}{\text{volume}}$ results

pressure

pressure x volume = a constant at constant temperature

ideal gas a gas which obeys Boyle's law (↓) exactly under all conditions of temperature (p.181) and pressure (p.30). Kinetic theory (p.188) shows that this will happen if the intermolecular forces (p.218) are zero, and the excluded volume effect (p.201) is also zero. Real gases behave very much like ideal gases if the pressure is not too high and the temperature is not too low.

Boyle's law for a fixed mass of gas at a fixed temperature (p.181), the pressure (p.30) of the gas will be inversely proportional (p.235) to its volume (p.55); i.e. the pressure multiplied by the volume will be a constant (p.234), if the temperature does not change. This can be shown experimentally by forcing some gas into a small volume, and measuring the pressure with a Bourdon gauge (p.31). Care must be taken to allow the gas to return to its starting temperature, as it will tend to heat up when forced into a small space.

Charles' law

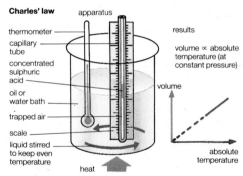

apparatus

thermometer

capillary tube

concentrated sulphuric acid

oil or water bath

trapped air

scale

liquid stirred to keep even temperature

heat

results

volume ∝ absolute temperature (at constant pressure)

volume

absolute temperature

Charles' law for a fixed mass of gas held under a fixed pressure (p.30), the volume (p.55) of the gas will be proportional (p.235) to the absolute temperature (p.184) of the gas. This can be shown experimentally by heating a small volume of gas trapped by a thread of sulphuric acid in a tube with a small bore (p.182), called a capillary tube. The acid keeps the gas dry.

pressure law

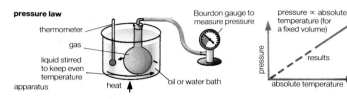

thermometer

gas

liquid stirred
to keep even
temperature

apparatus   heat   oil or water bath

Bourdon gauge to
measure pressure

pressure ∝ absolute
temperature (for
a fixed volume)

results

pressure

absolute temperature

pressure law for a fixed mass of gas held in a
container of fixed volume (p.55), the pressure
(p.30) will be proportional (p.235) to the absolute
temperature (p.184) of the gas. This can be
shown experimentally by heating a container of
gas fixed to a Bourdon gauge (p.31).

combined gas law if a fixed mass of gas starts at
a pressure (p.30) p_1, volume (p.55) V_1, and
absolute temperature (p.184) T_1, and is then
made to take up a volume V_2, where its pressure
is p_2, and its absolute temperature is T_2, then
$p_1 V_1 / T_1 = p_2 V_2 / T_2$.

equation of state one showing how changes in the
pressure (p.30), volume (p.55), mass and temperature (p.181) of a material affect each other.

equation of state for an ideal gas if the pressure
(p.30) of the gas is p, its volume (p.55) is V, its
absolute temperature (p.184) is T, and if there
are N moles (p.237) of the gas, then $pV = NRT$,
where R is the molar gas constant (↓).

molar gas constant a fundamental constant
(p.234), the constant of proportionality (p.235) in
the equation of state for an ideal gas (↑). It is also
equal to Boltzmann's constant (p.191) multiplied
by Avogadro's number (p.237). $R = 8.3$
$JK^{-1} mol^{-1}$, where R is the molar gas constant.

non-ideal gas a gas which does not obey Boyle's
law (p.199) under all conditions of temperature
(p.181) and pressure (p.30). All real gases are
non-ideal, but the difference is often small for
most temperatures and pressures. Non-ideal
behaviour is caused by the intermolecular forces
(p.218) tending to hold the gas molecules
(p.188) together. This means that the pressure
will be less than it would be if there were no such
forces. Non-ideal behaviour is also caused by
the excluded volume effect (↓).

excluded volume effect the failure of a gas to behave like an ideal gas (p.199) because of the volume (p.55) taken up by the molecules (p.188) of the gas themselves.

isotherm (*n*) a line which is drawn on a graph of pressure (p.30) against volume (p.55). An isotherm shows how the pressure changes with volume if the gas is held at a fixed temperature (p.181).

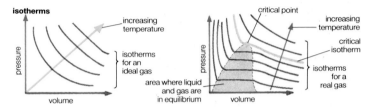

isotherms

pressure

volume

increasing temperature

isotherms for an ideal gas

critical point

increasing temperature

critical isotherm

isotherms for a real gas

area where liquid and gas are in equilibrium

pressure

volume

critical isotherm an isotherm (↑) which at one point is parallel (p.234) to the volume (p.55) axis, so that at this point a small change in volume will cause no change in pressure (p.30).

critical point the point at which the critical isotherm (↑) is parallel (p.234) to the volume (p.55) axis.

critical density the density (p.28) of a gas at its critical point (↑).

critical temperature the temperature (p.181) of the critical isotherm (↑). Above this temperature the material cannot be made into a liquid just by increasing the pressure (p.30). Below this temperature, if the density (p.28) is increased above the critical density (↑), liquid will then form.

ratio of specific heats the specific heat capacity (p.185) of a material when held at a fixed pressure (p.30) divided by its specific heat capacity when held in a fixed volume (p.55). The specific heat capacities are different because as the material will try to expand (p.214) when heated, extra heat will have to be supplied if the material *is* allowed to expand to make up for the work (p.17) done in pushing back the atmosphere (p.31) around the material.

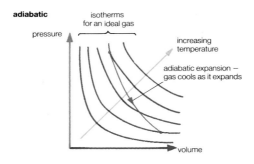

adiabatic isotherms for an ideal gas

pressure

increasing temperature

adiabatic expansion — gas cools as it expands

volume

adiabatic (*adj*) of a change in which no heat energy (p.18) enters or leaves a system. If a line is drawn on a graph of pressure (p.30) against volume (p.55), to show how pressure changes with volume in an adiabatic change, this line will always be steeper than the line for an isothermal (↓) change starting from the same point. Adiabatic changes are those which happen in systems which are thermally insulated (p.210), so heat energy cannot enter or leave, or changes which happen quickly, so there is no time for heat to enter or leave. For an ideal gas (p.199) in an adiabatic change, the quantity pV^γ is unchanged, where p is the pressure, V is the volume, and γ is the ratio of specific heats (p.201).

isothermal (*adj*) of a change in which the temperature (p.181) of a system does not change. Isothermal changes occur in systems which are in thermal contact (p.210) with a large store of heat energy (p.18), or when changes happen slowly, so there is time for the system to take in or give out heat to remain at a fixed temperature.

free expansion an expansion (p.214) in which a gas is allowed to expand into an empty space. This is an irreversible change (p.207) and the gas does no work (p.17) except for any work that is done against the intermolecular forces (p.218). For an ideal gas (p.199) there will be no change in temperature (p.181), but most real gases cool as they expand, though hydrogen and helium at room temperature get hotter rather than cooler.

free expansion

porous material controls flow of gas

gas expands into empty space, most gases become cooler as they expand

gas at high pressure

Boyle temperature

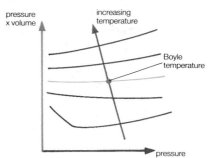

Boyle temperature the temperature (p.181) at which a non-ideal gas (p.200) comes closest to obeying Boyle's law (p.199). Below this temperature, the pressure (p.30) multiplied by the volume (p.55) will at first decrease as the pressure is increased. Above the Boyle temperature, the pressure multiplied by the volume increases with increasing pressure.

Joule-Kelvin effect the change in temperature (p.181) of a non-ideal gas (p.200) when it performs a free expansion (↑). This is caused by work (p.17) being done against the intermolecular forces (p.218). The energy to do this work comes from the kinetic energy (p.18) of the molecules (p.188) causing a drop in temperature. This is used to make liquids of gases which are above their critical points (p.201) and so cannot be made into liquids just by increasing the pressure. Hydrogen and helium have inversion temperatures (↓) below room temperature, and so must be cooled below their inversion temperatures by other methods before they can be cooled further by the Joule-Kelvin effect.

inversion temperature the temperature (p.181) below which the Joule-Kelvin effect (↑) causes the temperature of a gas to fall in a free expansion (↑). At temperatures higher than this the gas will become hotter rather than cooler in a free expansion.

thermodynamics (*n*) the study of heat and the way in which the flow of heat from one place to another is controlled by three laws called the laws of thermodynamics. Because these laws can be used for any system, the results of thermodynamics are true for a wide range of systems, however complicated the working of the system (*see zeroth law of thermodynamics* (p.181)).

first law of thermodynamics $\delta U = \delta Q + \delta W$, where δU is the change in internal energy ($\downarrow$) of a system, δQ is the amount of heat energy (p.18) entering the system, and δW is the amount of work (p.17) done on the system. The first law of thermodynamics is a result of the law of conservation of energy (p.18). In an adiabatic (p.202) change, $\delta Q = 0$. In an isothermal (p.202) change, $\delta U = 0$.

internal energy the energy in any material which is due to the kinetic energy (p.18) of the molecules (p.188) from which that material is made, and to any potential energy (p.17) from intermolecular forces (p.218) between or within those molecules. The internal energy of an object does not include any kinetic energy resulting from the motion of the whole object, or any potential energy because of the position of the object in any electric (p.97), magnetic (p.92) or gravitational field (p.24). The internal energy of an object depends only on the temperature (p.181) of the object.

second law of thermodynamics the amount of heat energy (p.18) going into or out of a system and the amount of work (p.17) done on or by that system are controlled by the temperatures (p.181) at which the system takes in or gives out heat. The second law of thermodynamics is usually stated in one of two forms, Kelvin's statement (p.207) and Clausius' statement (p.207). It can be shown, however, that these two statements are in fact the same law. The main result of the law is that no machine which uses heat energy can be completely efficient (p.20), even if there is no loss of energy through friction (p.15).

heat reservoir an imaginary object into which an unlimited amount of heat energy (p.18) can be placed, or from which an unlimited amount of heat energy can be taken, without causing any change of temperature (p.181). No real object can be a perfect heat reservoir, but any object which is much larger than the system which is moving heat energy to or from that object will behave similarly.

Carnot cycle

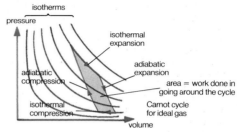

Carnot cycle a series of changes carried out on some material, usually taken to be an ideal gas (p.199). At the end of these changes the material is at the same temperature (p.181), pressure (p.30) and volume (p.55) as it was when it started. Heat energy (p.18) will have been moved from one heat reservoir (↑) to another, and some work (p.17) will have been turned into heat energy, or heat energy into work, depending on the direction in which the cycle is carried out. The stages in the Carnot cycle are: (i) an isothermal (p.202) expansion (p.214) with the system in thermal contact (p.210) with one heat reservoir. Heat energy is taken from this reservoir and changed into work; (ii) an adiabatic (p.202) expansion in which internal energy (↑) is changed to work and the temperature falls; (iii) an isothermal compression (p.214) in which work is changed to heat energy; (iv) an adiabatic compression in which work is used to return the internal energy of the material to its starting value, so that the cycle can be repeated.

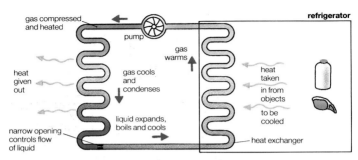

refrigerator (*n*) any machine used to remove heat energy (p.18) from an object, to lower the temperature (p.181) of that object. Most refrigerators work as a heat pump (↓), the lower temperature heat reservoir (p.205) being the object to be cooled, and the higher temperature reservoir being the outside air. The heat is moved from one to the other by allowing the liquid in the refrigerator to boil (p.192) close to the object to be cooled. Heat is then removed as latent heat of vaporization (p.194). A motor (p.120) then compresses (p.214) the vapour (p.195) back to a liquid, heating it at the same time. This heat is given off to the outside air by a heat exchanger (p.211) and the liquid can then be used again.

heat engine any machine which takes heat energy (p.18) in from some high temperature (p.181) area, often provided by burning a suitable material, and changes some of this energy into work (p.17). It gives out the rest of the energy as heat at a lower temperature. Because of the second law of thermodynamics (p.204), it is not possible to change all the heat energy into work. Some waste heat energy is always produced.

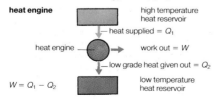

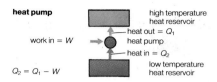

heat pump

work in = W

$Q_2 = Q_1 - W$

high temperature
heat reservoir
heat out = Q_1
heat pump
heat in = Q_2
low temperature
heat reservoir

heat pump any machine which uses work (p.17) to move heat from a place which is at a lower temperature (p.181), to a place at a higher temperature. Because of the second law of thermodynamics (p.204), it is not possible to do this without work being done.

Kelvin's statement of the second law of thermodynamics it is not possible to produce any system which does nothing but change heat completely into work (p.17).

Clausius' statement of the second law of thermodynamics it is not possible to produce any system which does nothing but make heat flow from a cooler to a hotter body.

absolute zero the lowest temperature (p.181) that it is possible to imagine. At this temperature, the pressure (p.30) and volume (p.55) of an ideal gas (p.199) would be zero, and all molecules (p.188) would have stopped moving.

third law of thermodynamics it is impossible to reach absolute zero (↑). The more work (p.17) that is used in cooling an object, the closer to absolute zero it can be cooled, but it is not possible actually to reach that temperature, even in a system which has perfect thermal insulation (p.210).

reversible change

piston does work
as gas expands   vacuum

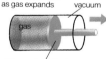

piston pushed slowly
back by gas pressure

reversible change a change which it is possible to imagine happening backwards, such as the expansion (p.214) of a gas pushing back the wall of a container and doing work (p.17). In a reversible change, the entropy (p.208) of a closed system does not change.

irreversible change

metal plate with
small hole

gas   vacuum

gas flows through hole

irreversible change a change which could not happen backwards, such as a container of gas suddenly being opened with all the gas flowing out into a vacuum (p.242), doing no work (p.17). In an irreversible change, the entropy (p.208) of a closed system will increase.

quasi-static change a change which happens so slowly that at all stages the system which is changing can be considered to be in thermodynamic equilibrium ($\downarrow$).

entropy

ordered arrangement
low entropy

disordered arrangement
high entropy

entropy (*n*) a quantity which measures the amount of order or disorder in a system. A more ordered system has a lower entropy. In a reversible change (p.207), the entropy of any closed system, including the whole universe, will not change, but in an irreversible change (p.207), the entropy of a closed system must increase. This means that the entropy of the universe must always increase.

thermodynamic equilibrium a state (p.192) in which all parts of a system which are in thermal contact (p.210) with each other are at the same temperature (p.181), so the system can be described without any doubt by its pressure (p.30), temperature, etc.

thermodynamic efficiency the amount of heat that is changed into useful work (p.17) by a machine, divided by the total amount of heat used by that machine. Even if there is no heat loss due to poor thermal insulation (p.210) or wasted work due to friction (p.15), the thermodynamic efficiency of a machine cannot be 100%. If the machine takes in heat from a heat reservoir (p.205) at an absolute temperature (p.184) T_1, and gives out heat at a lower absolute temperature T_2, then the largest thermodynamic efficiency that can be reached is $1 - (T_2/T_1)$.

low grade heat heat energy (p.18) in a heat reservoir (p.205) at a low temperature (p.181). It can be turned into work (p.17) only by a heat engine (p.206) which operates between this heat reservoir and one at an even lower temperature. If this second heat reservoir is not at a much lower temperature, the thermodynamic efficiency ($\uparrow$) of any heat engine using this heat will be low.

heat transfer the movement of heat energy (p.18) from one place to another. It can happen in any of three ways, called thermal conduction (↓), convection (p.210) and thermal radiation (p.211).

thermal conduction

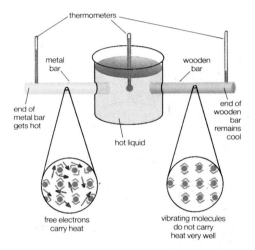

thermometers

metal bar

wooden bar

end of metal bar gets hot

end of wooden bar remains cool

hot liquid

free electrons carry heat

vibrating molecules do not carry heat very well

thermal conduction the movement of heat energy (p.18) through a material without there being any movement of that material itself.
thermal conductor a material in which thermal conduction (↑) happens easily. Metals are thermal conductors because when one end of a piece of metal is heated, the vibrations (p.242) of the atoms (p.139) at the hot end give energy to the free electrons (p.139) which in turn carry that energy to other atoms further down the metal. In non-metals, there are no free electrons, but heat energy can still be carried through a non-metal by the vibration of one atom being passed to the atoms around it by the intermolecular forces (p.218). This is a much less effective way of carrying the energy, so non-metals are not usually good thermal conductors.

thermal conductivity

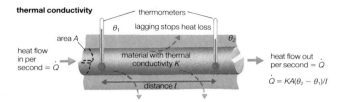

$$\dot{Q} = KA(\theta_2 - \theta_1)/l$$

thermal conductivity a measure of the ability of a material to carry heat by thermal conduction (p.209). The heat flow through a material is equal to $KA(\theta_2 - \theta_1)/l$, where A is the cross sectional area (p.233) of the material, θ_1 and θ_2 are the temperatures (p.181) of the material at two points separated by a distance l, and K is the thermal conductivity. SI unit (p.8): $Wm^{-1}K^{-1}$.

thermal insulation any material which is used to prevent the flow of heat into or out of a particular place, to keep something at a temperature (p.181) different from the temperature of the things around it.

thermal insulator a material which will not carry much heat by thermal conduction (p.209). It may thus be used for thermal insulation (↑). Non-metals which contain a lot of trapped air are particularly good thermal insulators, as air has a very low thermal conductivity (↑), but it must be held in place to prevent convection (↓).

lagging (*n*) another name for thermal insulation (↑), particularly when it is used around water pipes.

thermal contact the state of two objects when heat can easily flow from one to the other.

convection (*n*) the flow of heat from one place to another by the motion of a fluid (p.30). Most fluids become less dense (p.28) as they are heated, so if a fluid is heated near the bottom of a space in which it can move, the warm fluid will rise and cooler fluid will move in to take its place until the whole of the fluid is in motion. The only important material that becomes denser when heated is water in the temperature (p.181) range 0°C to 4°C.

thermal insulation

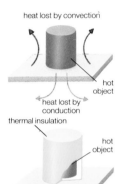

much less heat lost by convection and conduction

convection

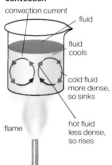

convection current a flow of fluid (p.30) caused by convection (↑).

forced convection convection (↑) in which the motion of the fluid (p.30) is helped by or is caused by something other than the change in density (p.28) of the fluid, for instance a motor (p.120).

heat exchanger

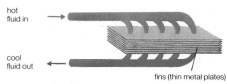

hot
fluid in

cool
fluid out

fins (thin metal plates)

heat exchanger anything which is made to allow heat energy (p.18) to pass from one fluid (p.30) to another. It is usually made of a series of narrow thermally conducting (p.209) pipes, through which one fluid moves, with the other fluid on the outside of the pipes. Thin metal plates, called *fins*, are sometimes used to increase the area in thermal contact (↑).

thermal radiation

all hot objects give off
thermal (infra-red) radiation

very hot objects also
produce visible light

Newton's law of cooling the heat loss by convection (↑) for an object in still air is proportional (p.235) to the difference in temperature (p.181) between the object and the things around it. This is an empirical (p.238) law and is true only for temperature differences up to about 30K. For higher temperature differences, up to about 300K, the heat loss is more nearly proportional to the temperature difference to the power of 5/4.

thermal radiation the electromagnetic radiation (p.241) given off by any body that has a temperature (p.181) above absolute zero (p.207). The amount of energy lost in this way depends on the surface of the material and on its temperature, but for temperatures from a few hundred to a few thousand kelvin (p.184), most of the electromagnetic radiation produced is in the infra-red (p.88) part of the electromagnetic spectrum (p.86).

effect of surfaces on thermal radiation dark and dull surfaces are the most effective for giving off thermal radiation (p.211). White or shiny surfaces will give off much less thermal radiation at the same temperature (p.181). Surfaces which are most effective at giving off radiation are also best at taking in thermal radiation. For these reasons, dark objects will get very hot in bright sunlight, but will cool quickly at night, particularly if the sky is clear, when the thermal radiation is not reflected (p.45) by clouds and absorbed again by the dark object.

effect of surfaces on thermal radiation

thermometer with black bulb reaches higher temperature than thermometer with white bulb

electric heater

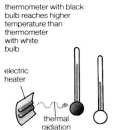

thermal radiation

sea breeze

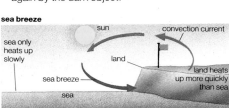

sun
convection current
sea only heats up slowly
land
sea breeze
land heats up more quickly than sea
sea

sea breeze a wind blowing off the sea onto the land, which is caused by a convection current (p.211). The land will heat up more quickly than the sea, because the land has a smaller heat capacity (p.185).

land breeze

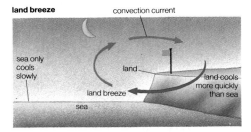

convection current
sea only cools slowly
land
land breeze
land cools more quickly than sea
sea

land breeze a wind blowing off the land onto the sea. At night the land cools down more rapidly than the sea, because the land has a lower heat capacity (p.185). This causes a convection current (p.211).

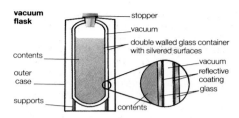

vacuum flask — stopper
vacuum
double walled glass container with silvered surfaces
contents
outer case
supports
vacuum
reflective coating
glass
contents

vacuum flask a double-walled container made for keeping hot materials hot or cold materials cold. The space between the two walls contains a vacuum (p.242) to stop heat flow by convection (p.210) or thermal conduction (p.209). The walls are covered with a reflective (p.45) surface to prevent thermal radiation (p.211) entering or leaving the container. When used to hold hot materials, a close-fitting lid is also used to stop convection through the top of the container, or cooling by evaporation (p.193). Also known as **thermos flask** or **Dewar flask**.

thermos flask = vacuum flask (↑).

Dewar flask = vacuum flask (↑).

temperature gradient the difference in temperature (p.181) between two points divided by the distance between them. The flow of heat energy by thermal conduction (p.209) is proportional (p.235) to the temperature gradient. SI unit (p.8): Km^{-1}.

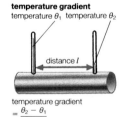

temperature gradient

temperature θ_1 temperature θ_2

distance l

temperature gradient
$= \dfrac{\theta_2 - \theta_1}{l}$

Leslie's cube a hollow metal cube with each face painted differently. The cube is filled with hot water and the amount of thermal radiation (p.211) given off by each surface can be found with a thermopile (p.106). This can be used to show the effect of surfaces on thermal radiation (p.211).

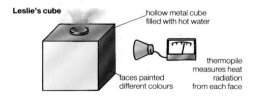

Leslie's cube

hollow metal cube filled with hot water

thermopile measures heat radiation from each face

faces painted different colours

expand (*v*) to become larger. **expansion** (*n*).
contract (*v*) to become smaller. **contraction** (*n*).
compress (*v*) to force to become smaller.
　compression (*n*).

thermal expansion

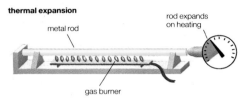

rod expands on heating

metal rod

gas burner

thermal expansion the expansion (↑) of an object
　caused by a change in temperature (p.181). As a
　material is heated, its molecules (p.188) move
　more and more quickly, and the average
　distance between them increases. Thermal
　expansion is largest in gases, if the gas is free to
　expand, and least in solids. The thermal
　expansion of a liquid is between that of a solid
　and a gas.
anomalous thermal expansion of water at
　temperatures (p.181) between 0°C and 4°C,
　water contracts (p.104) as it is heated, rather
　than expanding (↑). In this temperature range,
　water molecules (p.188) tend to form into groups
　of two or three held together by the electrostatic
　(p.95) forces (hydrogen bonding (p.220))
　between polar molecules (p.102).
linear expansivity the fractional change (p.232)
　in length of a solid for each degree of
　temperature (p.181) change. $a = \delta l/(l\delta\theta)$, where
　a is the linear expansivity, l is the length of the
　piece of material, and δl is the change in that
　length which is caused by a change in
　temperature $\delta\theta$.

**anomalous thermal
expansion of water**

volume

0°C　4°C
temperature

linear expansivity

linear expansivity $= a$

change in length δl
when temperature
increases by $\delta\theta$

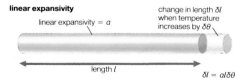

length l

$\delta l = a l \delta\theta$

measurement of thermal expansion in solids a rod of a material can be held firmly at one end and heated by passing steam through a larger tube around the material, or through the rod itself if it is hollow. The expansion (↑) can then be measured by using a micrometer screw gauge (p.9) which is firmly fixed in position near the free end of the rod. The micrometer is made to touch the rod before it is heated, screwed away from the rod to allow it room to expand, and then screwed back up to the rod. The difference in the readings on the micrometer before and after the rod has been heated is the change in length of the rod.

bimetallic strip

strips of different metal, held firmly together

rivets

when heated one metal expands more than the other, so strip bends

bimetallic strip two pieces of different metals, having different linear expansivities (↑), fixed firmly together. When the temperature (p.181) of the strip changes, one metal will expand (↑) or contract (↑) more than the other, so the strip will bend. A bimetallic strip can be used in a thermostat (↓).

thermostat

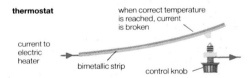

when correct temperature is reached, current is broken

current to electric heater

bimetallic strip

control knob

thermostat (*n*) a system for keeping something at a fixed temperature (p.181), usually by controlling a heater. Thermostats use some object which has some property, e.g. length, resistance (p.108), etc., which changes with temperature. A simple thermostat may use a bimetallic strip (↑) to control the flow of electricity to a heater.

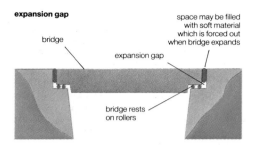

expansion gap

bridge

expansion gap

space may be filled
with soft material
which is forced out
when bridge expands

bridge rests
on rollers

expansion gap a space left between two objects
to prevent them being forced together when they
get hot and expand (p.214). Expansion gaps are
used in large bridges and in railway lines.

superficial expansivity the fractional change
(p.232) in the surface area of an object caused
by each degree of temperature (p.181) change.
It is equal to twice the linear expansivity (p.214).

cubic expansivity the fractional change (p.232) in
the volume (p.55) of a material caused by each
degree of temperature (p.181) change. For a
solid this is three times the linear expansivity
(p.214); for an ideal gas (p.199) held at a fixed
pressure (p.30) it is equal to the reciprocal of the
absolute temperature (p.184).

apparent expansion the thermal expansion
(p.214) of a fluid (p.30) which seems to have
taken place, before any account is taken of the
change in volume (p.55) of the container in which
the fluid was held.

absolute expansion the thermal expansion
(p.214) of a fluid (p.30) that has actually taken
place. This will not be the same as the expansion
that is measured, because of the expansion of
the measuring apparatus.

Pyrex (*n*) a type of glass which has a very low linear
expansivity (p.214). Unlike ordinary glass, it will
not break when suddenly heated or cooled.
Ordinary glass breaks because the different
expansion (p.214) or contraction (p.214) of
different parts of the glass, which have not had
time to reach the same temperature (p.181),
causes forces which are too large for the glass.

Meissner effect

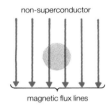

non-superconductor

magnetic flux lines

superconductor

no magnetic flux inside
a superconductor

**quantization of magnetic
fields in superconducting
systems**

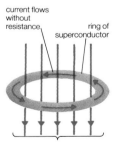

current flows
without
resistance

ring of
superconductor

only certain values of
magnetic flux are allowed

cryostat (*n*) a container for keeping a material at a low temperature (p.181). Cryostats usually take the form of a vacuum flask (p.213), or two vacuum flasks, one inside another, with liquid nitrogen in the space between them.

superconductor (*n*) a material which has no electrical resistance (p.108).

superconductivity (*n*) the disappearance of electrical resistance (p.108) at low temperatures (p.181).

transition temperature the temperature (p.181) below which a material becomes a superconductor (↑). The highest transition temperature for a pure metal is 12K, but some compounds (p.236) have much higher transition temperatures.

Meissner effect the absence of any magnetic field (p.92) inside a superconductor (↑).

high temperature superconductivity super-conductivity (↑) with a transition temperature (↑) high enough to be reached by cooling with liquid nitrogen or a similar material, rather than the much more expensive liquid helium.

superfluidity (*n*) the absence of viscosity (p.32) which is found in liquid helium when it is cooled below a temperature of 2.2K (called the *λ-point*).

quantization of magnetic fields in superconducting systems because of the loss of electrical resistance (p.108) in superconductors (↑), the wavefunctions (p.150) of electrons (p.139) in a ring of superconductor must be continuous. This means that the magnetic field in the ring can take only certain values.

SQUID (*abbr*) *s*uperconducting *q*uantum *i*nterference *d*evice. An instrument for measuring magnetic fields (p.92) using the quantization of magnetic fields in superconducting systems (↑).

BCS theory (*abbr*) the Bardeen-Cooper-Schrieffer theory (p.238) of superconductivity (↑), in which free electrons (p.139) in a metal at low temperature (p.181) form pairs, called Cooper pairs (↓), which move through the metal with no electrical resistance (p.108).

Cooper pair a pair of electrons (p.139) in the BCS theory (↑).

interatomic forces the forces between two or more atoms (p.139). At very small distances between the two atoms, the atoms repel (p.239) each other as the orbits (p.26) of their electrons (p.139) overlap. This is a result of the Pauli exclusion principle (p.141), which prevents two electrons from being in the same quantum (p.148) state. At larger distances, the atoms attract (p.239) each other as a result either of the bonding (p.221) between them, or, if there is no bonding, as a result of the van der Waals' force (↓) between them.

intermolecular force the force between two molecules (p.188). This will be the van der Waals' force (↓) for molecules which are not polar molecules (p.102), or hydrogen bonding (p.220) if the molecules are polar molecules.

van der Waals' force a weak attractive (p.239) force that exists between any two atoms (p.139) even if they are electrically neutral (p.95) and there is no bond (p.221) between them. It is a result of the electrostatic (p.95) forces between the induced dipoles (↓) in the atoms.

induced dipole an electric dipole (p.96) found in a neutral (p.95) atom (p.139) or a non-polar molecule (p.102) when in an electric field (p.97). Although the overall charge (p.95) is zero, at any given time the centre of negative charge will not be in the same place as the centre of positive charge, i.e. the nucleus (p.139). If the atom is in an electric field, the centres of charge will be pulled away from each other, but if there is no electric field, the strength of this electric dipole will average to zero, though at any moment its value will not usually be zero.

induced dipole

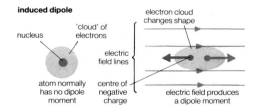

nucleus

'cloud' of electrons

electric field lines

atom normally has no dipole moment

centre of negative charge

electron cloud changes shape

electric field produces a dipole moment

induced dipole force the attraction (p.239) between the induced dipoles (↑) of two atoms (p.139). The atoms will always change the positions or the strength of their electric dipoles so they attract each other.

equilibrium separation the distance between two atoms (p.139) where there is no force between them, the attractive (p.239), long distance part of the interatomic force (↑) exactly balancing the repulsive (p.239), short distance part.

Lennard-Jones 6-12 potential a simple model to show the way in which the potential energy (p.17) of the interatomic force (↑) varies with the distance between two atoms (p.139). In this model the potential energy between the two atoms is given as $4\varepsilon[(a/r)^6 - 2(a/r)^{12}]$, where r is the distance between the two atoms and a is their equilibrium separation (↑); ε is the energy of a single bond (p.221) when the atoms are at equilibrium separation.

Lennard-Jones 6-12 potential (left)

interatomic forces and the thermal properties of materials (right)

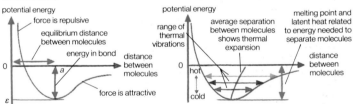

interatomic forces and the thermal properties of materials the melting point (p.192) and boiling point (p.192) of a material will depend on the amount of energy in the form of thermal (p.181) vibrations (p.242) needed to break a bond (p.221). The latent heat (p.193) will depend on the strength of the bonds being broken. The thermal expansion (p.214) of a solid material is produced by the asymmetry (p.232) about the equilibrium separation (↑) of the change of potential energy (p.17) with distance. When the energy is increased by the energy of thermal vibrations, the average distance between the atoms increases.

interatomic forces and the mechanical properties of materials

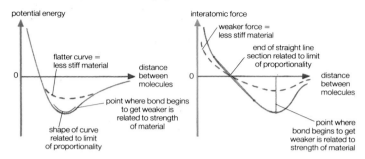

interatomic forces and the mechanical properties of materials the strength of a material depends on the force needed to break a bond (↓). This point is reached when the force between two atoms (p.139) no longer increases but gets weaker as the distance between them is increased. The material's stiffness depends on how rapidly the force between two atoms increases as the distance between them moves from the equilibrium separation (p.219). The limit of proportionality (p.235) is reached when the distance between the two atoms is so far from the equilibrium separation that the interatomic force (p.218) is no longer proportional to the distance from equilibrium separation.

hydrogen bonding a force of attraction (p.239) between polar molecules (p.102), which is particularly strong between molecules which contain a covalently bonded (↓) hydrogen atom (p.139), as such molecules are highly polar molecules. This force is stronger than the van der Waals' force (p.218), but less strong than covalent (↓), ionic (↓) or metallic bonding (↓).

hydrogen bonding

electrostatic force produces hydrogen bonding

polar molecule (e.g. hydrogen chloride)

ionic bonding bonding (↓) which produces a strong attractive (p.239) force between ions (p.139) of opposite charges (p.95) due to the electrostatic (p.95) forces between such ions. Ionically bonded materials form crystalline (p.229) solids with high melting points (p.192).

ionic bonding

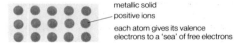

— negative ions

crystalline material (e.g. sodium chloride)

each ion held in place by electrostatic forces

— positive ions

metallic bonding

metallic solid

positive ions

each atom gives its valence electrons to a 'sea' of free electrons

metallic bonding the bonding (↓) that holds metal atoms (p.139) together in a solid. The atoms each give one or more of their valence electrons (p.140) to a 'sea' of electrons (p.139). The positive ions (p.139) form a crystalline (p.229) solid, but with a lower melting point (p.192) than most ionically bonded (↑) solids.

covalent bond

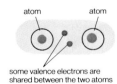

atom   atom

some valence electrons are shared between the two atoms

covalent bonding the bonding (↓) between two or more atoms (p.139) in which one or more electrons (p.139) are shared between the atoms to produce a strong bond (↓) between the atoms in a single molecule (p.188). If the electrons in the bond spend most of their time close to one atom, the molecule produced will be a polar molecule (p.102). Most covalent bonds are very strong but produce separate molecules rather than solid materials. Important exceptions to this are diamond, an allotrope (p.193) of carbon, and silicon dioxide, both of which have high melting points (p.192) due to the strength of the covalent bonds.

bond (*n*) a connection between two atoms (p.139) holding them together.

bonding (*n*) any one of the ways in which atoms (p.139) can be held together.

surface tension the force produced in the surface of a liquid because of the unbalanced intermolecular forces (p.218) near the surface. A molecule (p.188) near the surface feels forces pulling it towards the centre of the liquid, so the liquid behaves as if it was contained in an elastic (p.224) skin. For this reason, small objects, e.g. some insects, are able to rest on top of a water surface, and a liquid drop will tend to take on a spherical shape.

coefficient of surface tension a measure of the strength of the surface tension (↑) effects in a given liquid. The coefficient of surface tension is the force per metre length acting in the liquid surface at 90° on one side of a line drawn along the surface. SI unit (p.8): Nm^{-1}.

adhesion (*n*) the force of molecules (p.188) in a liquid being pulled towards the solid in which or on which the liquid is held. It is this force of adhesion which causes the capillary effect (↓) in most liquids and which causes some liquids to spread out and wet any surface on which they are placed.

cohesion (*n*) the force of one molecule (p.188) in a liquid being pulled towards others in the same liquid. It is this cohesion which causes surface tension (↑).

capillary effect the change in the level of that part of a liquid which is held in a narrow tube. The narrower the tube the larger the effect. Most liquids will rise up the tube, but if the cohesion (↑) is larger than the adhesion (↑), as it is in mercury, the level inside the tube will be lower than outside. If *h* is the height of rise in a tube of radius *r* with a liquid of density (p.28) ρ and coefficient of surface tension (↑) γ, then $h = 2\gamma/(r\rho g)$, where *g* is the acceleration due to gravity (p.12). This effect also occurs in porous (p.242) materials.

surface tension

pin floats on water surface supported by surface tension

surface tension holds liquids in drops

coefficient of surface tension

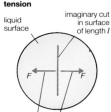

surface tension force F on each side of cut

$$\text{surface tension} = \frac{F}{l}$$

adhesion, cohesion

adhesion less than cohesion, liquid forms drops

adhesion more than cohesion, liquid spreads out

capillary effect

meniscus

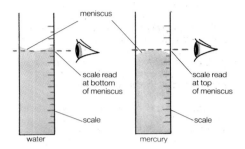

meniscus[2] (*n*) the curved surface on a liquid in a
  narrow container. For most liquids the level of the
  liquid is lower at the centre than at the edges, but
  for mercury the liquid level is higher in the centre
  than at the edges. Containers used for
  measuring the volume (p.55) of liquids are
  marked so that the correct volume is found by
  reading from the bottom of the meniscus, except
  for mercury, where the top should be used.

excess pressure the amount by which the
  pressure (p.30) in one place is greater than in
  another, in particular the difference in pressure
  between the inside and the outside of a bubble
  (↓).

bubble (*n*) a space filled with gas inside a liquid or
  separated from other gas by a thin layer of liquid.
  Because of surface tension (↑), the pressure
  (p.30) inside the bubble will be greater than the
  pressure outside. For a bubble in a liquid, the
  excess pressure (↑) is $2\gamma/r$, while for a bubble in
  gas the excess pressure is $4\gamma/r$, where *r* is the
  radius of the bubble and *γ* is the coefficient of
  surface tension (↑).

bubble

bubbles in a liquid

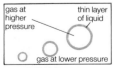

bubbles in a gas

elasticity (*n*) the property of a material which returns to its original size and shape after it has been stretched or compressed (p.214). **elastic** (*adj*).

tension (*n*) a force which tends to stretch a material.

in tension the state (p.192) of a material which is experiencing a force of tension (↑).

Hooke's law for materials that obey the law, the change in length of an object is proportional (p.235) to the force causing the change. All objects obey the law for small changes in length, but only some, e.g. springs, obey it for larger changes.

spring constant the constant of proportionality (p.235) in Hooke's law (↑), which measures how much an object will change its length for a given force. $F = kx$, where F is the force, k is the spring constant, and x is the extension (↓).

elastic limit the largest force which an object can experience and still return to its original shape and size after the force is no longer acting on it.

limit of proportionality the largest force which an object can experience and still change its length according to Hooke's law (↑).

elastic potential energy[2] the potential energy (p.17) stored in an object due to an elastic (↑) change in its shape or size. The elastic potential energy in an object which obeys Hooke's law (↑) is one half the force times the extension (↓). For a system with a spring constant (↑) k with extension (↑) x, the elastic potential energy is $\frac{1}{2}kx^2$.

extension (*n*) the increase in length of an object caused by a force. **extend** (*v*).

tensile stress the force acting to extend (↑) an object divided by the cross sectional area (p.233) of the object. SI unit (p.8): pascal (p.30).

tensile strain the change in length of an object caused by a tensile stress (↑) divided by its length when no force acts on it. Tensile strain is a pure number and has no unit, as it is one length divided by another.

elasticity

1 elastic material

2 material stretched

3 material returns
to original shape

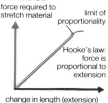

Hooke's law

force required to
stretch material

limit of
proportionality

Hooke's law:
force is
proportional to
extension

change in length (extension)

elastic potential energy

force

area =
elastic
potential
energy

change in length

tensile stress

area A

tensile stress $= \dfrac{F}{A}$ force F

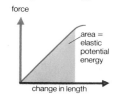

tensile strain

change in
length δl

length l

tensile strain $= \dfrac{\delta l}{l}$

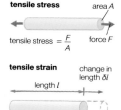

bulk stress

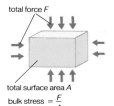

total force F

total surface area A

bulk stress $= \dfrac{F}{A}$

shear

object changes shape

equal and opposite forces with different lines of action

shear stress

area A force F

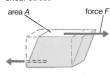

shear stress $= \dfrac{F}{A}$

shear strain

distance δl

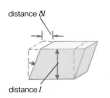

distance l

shear strain $= \dfrac{\delta l}{l}$

Young's modulus a measure of the elasticity (↑) of a material which does not depend on the shape or size of the piece of material. Young's modulus is equal to the tensile stress (↑) divided by the tensile strain (↑), for any tensile stress and tensile strain up to the limit of proportionality (↑) of the material. SI unit (p.8): pascal (p.30).

bulk stress the force acting to make the volume (p.55) of an object smaller divided by the area over which that force acts. SI unit (p.8): pascal (p.30).

bulk strain the change in volume (p.55) of an object caused by a bulk stress (↑) divided by its volume when there is no force on it.

bulk modulus bulk stress (↑) divided by bulk strain (↑); a measure of how easily the volume (p.55) of a material can be changed by a force acting to compress (p.214) it. SI unit (p.8): pascal (p.30).

isothermal bulk modulus of an ideal gas for an ideal gas (p.199) held at a fixed temperature (p.181), the bulk modulus (↑) of the gas is equal to the pressure (p.30) of the gas.

adiabatic bulk modulus of an ideal gas for an ideal gas (p.199) where no heat energy (p.18) can enter or leave the gas, the bulk modulus (↑) is equal to the pressure (p.30) multiplied by the ratio of specific heats (p.201).

shear (*n*) a change in shape caused by two equal and opposite forces having different lines of action (p.239). **shear** (*v*).

shear stress the force causing a shear (↑) divided by the area of one of the two surfaces which move over each other in the shear. SI unit (p.8): pascal (p.30).

shear strain the distance moved by one of the two surfaces that move over each other in a shear (↑), divided by the distance between those surfaces.

shear modulus the shear stress (↑) divided by the shear strain (↑); a measure of how easily the shape of an object made of a given material can be changed. SI unit (p.8): pascal (p.30). Also known as **modulus of rigidity**.

modulus of rigidity = shear modulus (↑).

plastic (*n,adj*) a material which does not return to its original shape or size after any force acting on it to change its shape is no longer present, e.g. polythene.

brittle (*adj*) of a material which breaks before reaching its elastic limit (p.224), e.g. cast iron.

malleable (*adj*) of a material which can easily be beaten into any desired shape, e.g. brass.

plastic

1 plastic material

2 material stretched

3 material does not return to old shape

ductile

1 ductile material

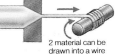

2 material can be drawn into a wire

ductile (*adj*) of a material which can be drawn out into wires, e.g. copper.

flexible (*adj*) of a material which can have its shape or size changed by a force acting on it, but which will then return to its original shape and size when the force is no longer acting on it, e.g. steel.

tough (*adj*) of a material which is not easily broken or cracked. When a tough material is stretched past its elastic limit (p.224), it will deform (↓) plastically (↑), e.g. nylon.

brittle

1 brittle material

2 material stretched

3 material breaks before elastic limit is reached

permanent set

force

material stretched past elastic limit

force increasing

force gets smaller

material does not return to starting length

change in length

permanent set

malleable

1 malleable material

2 material can be beaten into new shape

permanent set the change in size produced in a plastic (↑) deformation (↓) after the deforming force no longer acts.

deform (*v*) to change the size or shape of something. **deformation** (*n*).

yield point

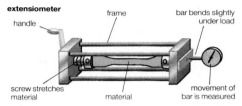

force

yield point

change in length

yield point the point where the force needed to produce further deformation (↑) of an object begins to get less, so if a steadily increasing force is used, the material will break once this force reaches the yield point.

breaking stress the tensile stress (p.224) at which a material breaks.

extensiometer

handle

frame

bar bends slightly under load

screw stretches material

material

movement of bar is measured

extensiometer (*n*) an instrument for measuring the force produced by stretching a material by a given amount. An I-shaped piece of material is stretched by a screw, and the force measured from the elastic (p.224) bending of a much thicker bar.

dislocation (*n*) a point or line in the crystalline (p.229) structure of a material which is not perfect.

edge dislocation

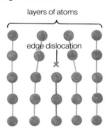

layers of atoms

edge dislocation

edge dislocation a dislocation (↑) where one layer of atoms (p.139) comes to a stop.

screw dislocation a dislocation (↑) where the atoms (p.139) of a single layer no longer form a flat surface, but form a twisted surface along which it is possible to move continuously from one layer of atoms to the next.

slip (*n*) a plastic (↑) deformation (↑) in a crystal (p.229) where layers of atoms (p.139) move to fill a dislocation (↑) one layer at a time, so that in effect the dislocation moves through the material in the opposite direction.

slip

edge dislocation

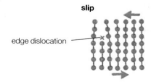

rubber (*n*) a material which can be deformed (p.226) a long way before reaching its elastic limit (p.224), the stiffness increasing as the material is deformed. Rubber is made of long molecules (p.188) which are usually twisted, but which become straight when the material is stretched.

glass (*n*) a material in which the molecules (p.188) are not arranged in any regular structure, but at random (p.235). This makes the material more like a liquid, but with the intermolecular forces (p.218) being strong enough for the material to appear as a solid. A glass will flow like a liquid, but only very slowly at normal temperatures (p.181). On heating, a glass has no melting point (p.192), but gradually becomes softer.

anneal (*v*) to heat and then allow to cool slowly. The vibration (p.242) of the atoms (p.139) in the material when it is hot reduces the number of dislocations (p.227) and makes the material easier to work.

quench (*v*) to heat and then cool suddenly. Dislocations (p.227) are then locked into position, producing a hard, brittle (p.226) material.

work hardening the hardening of a material which is usually malleable (p.226), but which becomes brittle (p.226) when it has been worked. Dislocations become pinned (↓) and twisted around one another. The material can be made less brittle again by annealing (↑).

pinned (*adj*) of the state of a dislocation (p.227) unable to move further through the material, usually because of a point defect (↓).

composite (*adj*) made up of two or more different materials.

point defect a fault which, unlike an edge dislocation (p.227) or screw dislocation (p.227), is found only at a point in a crystal (↓), such as an interstitial atom (↓) or an atom (p.139) missing from a position in a lattice (↓).

interstitial atom an atom (p.139) which is not at one of the positions in a crystal (↓) lattice (↓), but between these positions. Such an atom may be an atom of a different element (p.139) from that of which most of the material is made, e.g. a carbon atom in steel.

anneal

1 material heated . . .

2 ...and allowed to cool slowly

3 becomes easier to work

quench

1 material heated . . .

2 . . . and cooled quickly

3 becomes hard but brittle

composite

glassfibre, a composite material   plastic

thin glass threads

interstitial atom

atoms packed closely together (e.g. iron)

interstitial atom (e.g. carbon)

crystals

tetrahedral
(e.g. diamond)

hexagonal

cubic
(e.g. sodium chloride)

cubic close packed

layers of atoms in
cubic close packed crystal

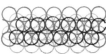

half atom 1/8 atom
at centre of at each
each face corner

cubic close packed unit cell

crystallography (*n*) the study of crystals (↓).
crystal (*n*) a material in which the atoms (p.139) are arranged in an ordered way. A piece of such material may have a shape which is related to the way in which the atoms are arranged.
crystalline (*adj*).

polycrystalline, grain boundary

crystalline
arrangement
of atoms

grain boundary

polycrystalline (*adj*) of a material made of many small crystalline (↑) pieces, each having an ordered arrangement of atoms (p.139) but an irregular shape. Metals are usually polycrystalline.
grain boundary the border between crystal (↑) pieces in a polycrystalline (↑) material.
lattice (*n*) an ordered arrangement of points in space. In a crystal (↑) these are the points where atoms (p.139) are found.
close packed of a crystal (↑) in which atoms (p.139) are packed as closely together as possible. In a close packed crystal containing only one type of atom, which is spherical, the space filling ratio (p.230) is 0.74.
cubic close packed of a close packed (↑) crystal (↑) in which atoms (p.139) are placed in layers with each atom having six near neighbours in that layer. The atoms in the next layer lie in the spaces in the first layer, and a third layer of atoms sits in the spaces in the second layer, but with the atoms not directly above those in the first layer. Such a structure is described as *ABCABC* .... The unit cell (p.230) is a cube with one eighth of an atom at each corner and half an atom in the centre of each face. Also known as **face centred cubic**.
face centred cubic = cubic close packed (↑).
f.c.c. (*abbr*).

hexagonal close packed

layers of atoms in a hexagonal close packed crystal

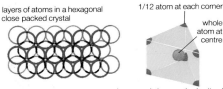

1/12 atom at each corner

whole atom at centre

hexagonal close packed unit cell

hexagonal close packed of a close packed (p.229) crystal (p.229) in which atoms (p.139) are placed in layers with each atom having six near neighbours in that layer. The atoms in the next layer lie in the spaces in the first layer, and the third layer of atoms sits in the spaces in the second layer directly above the first layer. Such a lattice (p.229) is described as *ABABA* .... The unit cell ($\downarrow$) is made in the shape of a triangular prism (p.68) with one twelfth of an atom at each corner and an atom in the centre. **h.c.p.** (*abbr*).

simple cubic of a crystal (p.229) where the unit cell ($\downarrow$) is a cube with one eighth of an atom (p.139) at each corner. The space filling ratio ($\downarrow$) is low, only 0.52.

body centred cubic of a crystal (p.229) where each atom (p.139) is surrounded by eight near neighbours. The unit cell ($\downarrow$) is a cube with one eighth of an atom at each corner and an atom in the middle. The space filling ratio ($\downarrow$) is 0.68. **b.c.c.** (*abbr*).

amorphous solid a solid which is not crystalline (p.229), but where the atoms (p.139) are arranged at random (p.235).

space filling ratio the volume (p.55) of atoms (p.139) in a crystal (p.229) divided by the volume of the whole crystal. The atoms are taken to be spherical and all of the same size. Also known as **packing fraction**.

packing fraction = space filling ratio ($\uparrow$).

unit cell the smallest part of a crystal (p.229) lattice (p.229) which shows how the atoms (p.139) are arranged in the crystal. Also known as **primitive cell**.

primitive cell = unit cell ($\uparrow$).

simple cubic

1/8 atom at each corner

simple cubic unit cell

body centred cubic

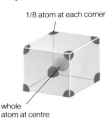

1/8 atom at each corner

whole atom at centre

body centred cubic unit cell

X-ray diffraction

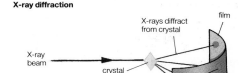

X-rays diffract
from crystal

film

X-ray
beam

crystal

pattern of spots allows
arrangement of atoms
in crystal to be found

X-ray diffraction the diffraction (p.50) of X-rays
(p.89) from a crystal (p.229). Each atom (p.139)
in the crystal diffracts X-rays, but there is
constructive (p.48) interference (p.48) between
these only in certain directions, given by Bragg's
law (↓). Measurement of the directions in which
X-rays of known wavelength (p.43) are diffracted
gives information about the arrangement of
atoms in the crystal and about the nature of the
atoms.

Bragg's law X-rays (p.89) diffracted (p.50) from
different layers of atoms (p.139) in a crystal
(p.229) will interfere (p.48) constructively (p.48) if
$2d\sin\theta = n\lambda$, where d is the distance between
the layers of atoms, λ is the wavelength (p.43) of
the X-rays, n is a whole number, and θ is the
angle between the X-rays and the layers of
atoms as they enter and leave the crystal.

Bragg's law

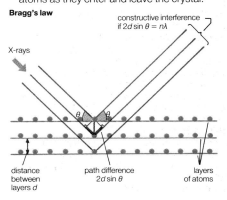

constructive interference
if $2d \sin \theta = n\lambda$

X-rays

θ θ

distance
between
layers d

path difference
$2d \sin \theta$

layers
of atoms

modulus (*n*) a value of a quantity taken as being positive, whether the quantity was positive or negative. Also used for the magnitude (p.10) of a vector (p.10).

integer (*n*) a whole number.

fractional change the change in some quantity divided by the original value of that particular quantity.

ratio (*n*) the size of one quantity compared to that of some other quantity. Ratio may be expressed as a number or as a pair of whole numbers. E.g. if one quantity is twice another quantity, the ratio between them is 2 or 2:1.

infinitesimal (*adj*) smaller than the smallest imaginable.

symmetry

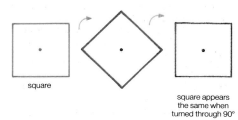

square

square appears
the same when
turned through 90°

symmetry (*n*) the property of an object or a system on which some action can be performed without causing any change in the object or system. E.g. a square appears unchanged when turned through an angle of 90° about its centre. **symmetrical** (*adj*).

asymmetry (*n*) the absence of symmetry (↑) in an object or system.

axis of symmetry a line about which an object can be turned and appear not to change. E.g. the axis of symmetry of a cylinder is a line through its centre at 90° to the flat circular surfaces of the cylinder.

radian (*n*) a unit (p.8) of angle. A complete circle, 360°, is 2π radian. In physics, angles, e.g. phase differences (p.37), are often measured in radians.

axis of symmetry

cylinder

axis of symmetry

oblate

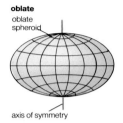

oblate
spheroid

axis of symmetry

prolate

prolate
spheroid

axis of symmetry

cross section

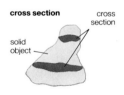

cross
section

solid
object

projection

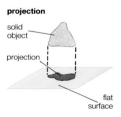

solid
object

projection

flat
surface

subtend

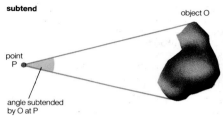

object O

point
P

angle subtended
by O at P

subtend (*v*) to take up an angle as seen from a given point. The angle subtended by an object at a given point is the angle between two lines drawn from that point to the edges of the object.

plane (*n*) a flat surface. **plane** (*adj*).

spheroid (*n*) a sphere which has been stretched or flattened. **spheroidal** (*adj*).

oblate (*adj*) of a spheroid (↑) which has the shape of a flattened sphere. Most planets (p.26) are oblate spheroids.

prolate (*adj*) of a spheroid (↑) which has the shape of a stretched sphere.

cross section the flat surface that is produced by cutting through a solid object.

cross sectional area the area of a cross section (↑).

projection (*n*) the mathematical process of showing a three-dimensional shape on a flat surface. **project** (*v*).

component (*n*) the length of line produced when a vector (p.10) is projected (↑) onto a given direction.

component

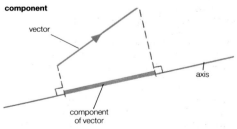

vector

axis

component
of vector

parabola (*n*) an open curve which can be produced by making a cross section (p.233) of a cone along a surface parallel (↓) to the side of the cone. $y = x^2$ is the equation of a parabola centred on the origin. **parabolic** (*adj*).

hyperbola (*n*) an open curve which can be produced by making a cross section (p.233) of a cone along a surface which makes a smaller angle with the axis of symmetry (p.232) of the cone than the sides of the cone itself. **hyperbolic** (*adj*).

ellipse (*n*) a closed curve, in the shape of a flattened circle, which can be produced by making a cross section (p.233) of a cone along a surface which makes a larger angle with the axis of symmetry (p.232) of the cone than the sides of the cone itself. **elliptic** (*adj*).

conic section any curve which can be produced by making a cross section (p.233) of a cone, i.e. a circle, ellipse (↑), parabola (↑) or hyperbola (↑). An object moving under the force of the gravity (p.23) of a single body will move along a curve which is a conic section.

sinusoidal (*adj*) of a quantity which changes in a way similar to the sine function in mathematics.

perpendicular (*adj*) at an angle of 90°.

parallel (*adj*) of two lines or planes (p.233) which lie in the same direction and so are a fixed distance apart.

normal (*n*) a line drawn at an angle of 90° to a surface. **normal** (*adj*).

linear (*adj*) of a mathematical relationship which appears as a straight line when shown on a graph. If two quantities are linearly related, then a given change in one of them will always cause a fixed change in the other. If x and y are linearly related, then $y = mx + c$, where m is called the *gradient* of the line on the graph and c is a constant (↓), the value of y when $x = 0$.

constant (*n*) a number whose value does not change in a calculation. **constant** (*adj*).

universal constant a constant (↑) whose value is the same at all times and in all places. Also known as **fundamental constant**.

fundamental constant = universal constant (↑).

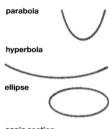

parabola

hyperbola

ellipse

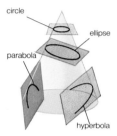

conic section

circle

ellipse

parabola

hyperbola

perpendicular

90°

the two lines are perpendicular

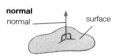

normal

normal

surface

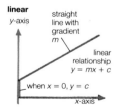

linear

y-axis

straight line with gradient m

linear relationship $y = mx + c$

when $x = 0$, $y = c$

x-axis

proportional

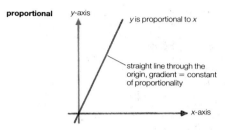

y-axis

y is proportional to x

straight line through the
origin, gradient = constant
of proportionality

x-axis

proportional (*adj*) of two quantities which are
related in such a way that when one of the
quantities is multiplied by a given number, the
other will be multiplied by the same number. A
graph of two quantities which are proportional
will be a straight line which passes through the
origin, the gradient of the line being equal to the
constant of proportionality (↓). **proportion** (*n*).
Also known as **directly proportional**.

directly proportional = proportional (↑).

inversely proportional of two quantities where
one is proportional (↑) to the reciprocal (↓) of the
other.

reciprocal (*n*) one divided by the quantity
concerned.

constant of proportionality the ratio (p.232)
between two proportional (↑) quantities. This
does not change as the quantities themselves
change. Since multiplying one quantity by any
number causes the other to be multiplied by the
same number, the ratio stays the same.

rate of change the change in a quantity divided by
the time over which it takes place, particularly
where the time taken is infinitesimal (p.232).

maximum, minimum

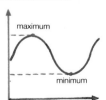

maximum

minimum

maximum (*n*) the largest value reached by a
quantity.

minimum (*n*) the smallest value reached by a
quantity.

probability (*n*) a measure of how likely it is that a
given event will take place. If the event is
impossible, it has a probability of zero; if it is
certain, it has a probability of one.

random (*adj*) of a system where events take place
or objects are arranged with no pattern.

chemistry (*n*) the study of the properties of elements (p.139), and the ways atoms (p.139) join together to form compounds (↓). **chemical** (*adj*).

chemical reaction the coming together of two or more elements (p.139) or compounds (↓), or the breaking down of a compound, e.g. by heating, so that although the number of atoms (p.139) of each element does not change, the atoms are joined together in different ways after the reaction.

chemical symbol one or two letters used as an abbreviation for the name of an element.

reactive (*adj*) of a material which is easily changed by a chemical reaction (↑).

stable (*adj*) of a system which is not easily changed, e.g. by a chemical reaction (↑) or radioactive (p.158) decay (p.158).

alloy

copper tin
(soft materials)   melt together   bronze
(a hard alloy)

copper
and tin
atoms
arranged
at random

alloy (*n*) a mixture (↓) of two or more metals. The atoms (p.139) of the different elements (p.139) are arranged at random (p.235). Alloys can be made with many useful properties and are often harder than the metals from which they are made. E.g. bronze is an alloy of the elements copper and tin.

compound (*n*) a material made from more than one element (p.139) where the ratio (p.232) between the numbers of atoms (p.139) of the different elements is fixed by the chemistry (↑) of the elements in the compound.

compound

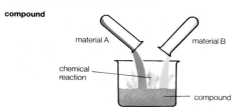

material A   material B

chemical
reaction

compound

mixture

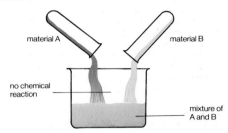

material A   material B

no chemical
reaction

mixture of
A and B

mixture (*n*) a material made from more than one
element (p.139) where there is no fixed ratio
(p.232) between the numbers of atoms (p.139)
of the different elements.

mole (*n*) the SI unit (p.8) of amount of material. One
mole of atoms (p.139) of the isotope (p.156)
carbon-12 has a mass of exactly 12 gram by
definition (p.238). One mole of any object is
about 6.02 x 10^{23} of them. **mol** (*abbr*).

Avogadro's number the number of objects in one
mole (↑). L = 6.02 x 10^{23}, where L is
Avogadro's number.

solution

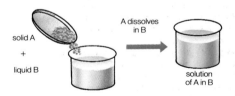

solid A

+

liquid B

A dissolves
in B

solution
of A in B

solution (*n*) a mixture (↑) where single atoms
(p.139), ions (p.139) or molecules (p.188) are
mixed in a liquid, so the solution is also a liquid.

ionic solution a solution (↑) which contains ions
(p.139). E.g. when sodium chloride is dissolved
(↓) in water, the solution contains ions from the
atoms (p.139) of sodium (Na^+) and from the
atoms of chlorine (Cl^-).

dissolve (*v*) to form a solution (↑).

physics (*n*) the part of science concerned with the properties of energy and matter and with the relationships between them. **physical** (*adj*).

law of physics a law which is thought to be obeyed through all of nature. Some laws are only obeyed under certain conditions, but are still always obeyed if the stated conditions are met.

theory (*n*) an idea, often expressed in a mathematical form, which is claimed to be a law of physics (↑).

empirical (*adj*) of a result which comes from experiment without any supporting theory (↑).

thought experiment an experiment which cannot actually be performed, because suitable apparatus cannot be produced. The supposed results of a thought experiment are used in talking about the possible results of a theory (↑). E.g. in Heisenberg's microscope experiment (p.151), no real microscope (p.74) would actually be suitable for the experiment, but the theory (↑) of how a microscope works can be used to explain some ideas in quantum mechanics (p.150). Also known as **gedankenexperiment**.

gedankenexperiment (*n*) = thought experiment (↑).

fundamental[2] (*adj*) of a piece of physics (↑) which cannot be explained by other pieces of physics, but which is used as a starting point for other pieces of physics.

paradox (*n*) a result which appears to break some law of physics (↑), but which in fact does not, the law having been incorrectly used for the system producing the paradoxical result. **paradoxical** (*adj*).

define (*v*) to fix the meaning of, or the value of, a particular quantity. E.g. the newton (p.14) is defined as the force which causes a mass of one kilogram to accelerate (p.12) at $1 \, \text{m s}^{-2}$. **definition** (*n*).

neglect (*v*) to leave out a certain effect, particularly from a calculation. This is usually done because the effect is too small to change the result of the calculation very much, and is too difficult to include in the calculation.

mechanics (*n*) the part of physics (↑) that deals with solid objects and the way they move, particularly under spring forces, and the forces of gravity (p.23) and friction (p.15). **mechanical** (*adj*).

load (*n*) an object or part of a circuit (p.104) on which work (p.17) is done or into which energy is placed.

static (*adj*) not moving.

dynamic (*adj*) moving or changing.

uniform (*adj*) not changing.

pendulum (*n*) a system containing a mass supported in such a way that it can perform simple harmonic motion (p.35), particularly a simple pendulum (p.36).

line of action

force   line of action

line of action the line which shows the way in which a force acts. A force acts in the direction of its line of action, and the moment (p.19) of the force about any point on the line of action is zero.

attraction

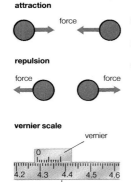

force

repulsion

force   force

vernier scale

vernier

0

4.2   4.3   4.4   4.5   4.6

main scale

reading = 4.287

attraction (*n*) a force which tries to pull two objects together. **attract** (*v*), **attractive** (*adj*).

repulsion (*n*) a force which tries to push two objects apart. **repel** (*v*), **repulsive** (*adj*).

vernier scale a scale made of two parts, a long main scale, and a smaller scale, called the vernier, which takes the place of a pointer and has ten marks in the space taken by nine marks on the main scale. The main scale is read against the first (zero) mark of the vernier. To find the number of tenths of the unit (p.8) used in the main scale, the vernier is looked at to see which of its marks lines up exactly with one of the marks on the main scale. E.g. if the third mark on the vernier lines up with a mark on the main scale, the measurement is some whole number of units plus 0.3 units.

parallax (*n*) an effect which results from the change in position of the person making the measurements concerned. Parallax results from the same system being seen from different positions.

parallax error

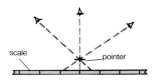

scale — pointer

parallax error an incorrect reading from a measuring instrument which is produced as a result of the instrument not being viewed from the correct position. On instruments which use a pointer and scale, a mirror may be fixed to the scale. When the image (p.64) of the pointer in the mirror is hidden behind the pointer, the instrument is being viewed from the correct position, and there will be no parallax error.

calibrate (*v*) to put marks on a scale in the correct places, or to change an instrument in some other way so the scale can be read correctly.

accurate (*adj*) of an instrument which gives readings which are close to the correct values of the quantities that are being measured. **accuracy** (*n*).

sensitive (*adj*) of an instrument which is able to detect small changes in the quantity that are being measured. A sensitive instrument is not necessarily accurate (↑). **sensitivity** (*n*).

conserve (*v*) to keep the same. Laws of physics (p.238) in which a quantity is conserved are very important. **conservation** (*n*).

alternate (*v*) to change repeatedly, particularly a sinusoidal (p.234) change between positive and negative values.

core (*n*) the central part of an object, e.g. a planet (p.26), a nuclear reactor (p.167) or a solenoid (p.114), where any core is usually made of a ferromagnetic (p.93) material.

sink

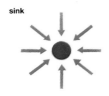

flux

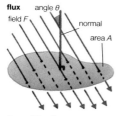

flux = $FA\cos\theta$

radiation

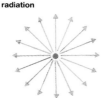

radiation spreads out
from a point in
straight lines

sink (*n*) a place where something is taken in or
disappears.

field (*n*) an effect which acts over a part of space,
e.g. electric field (p.97).

flux (*n*) the strength of a field (↑) multiplied by an
area multiplied by the cosine of the angle
between the direction of the field and the normal
(p.234) to that area.

radiation (*n*) any wave (p.42) or particle which is
given off from a point and spreads out in straight
lines. Any form of radiation will obey the inverse
square law (↓). Particularly used for infra-red
(p.88) electromagnetic (p.115) radiation, also
known as thermal radiation (p.211), and ionizing
(p.139) radiation, also known as nuclear (p.139)
radiation.

inverse square law

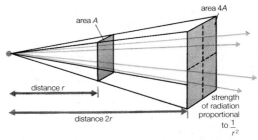

inverse square law the strength of any radiation
(↑) coming from a point and travelling through a
material where it is not absorbed (p.242) will be
inversely proportional (p.235) to the square of the
distance from that point.

induce (*v*) the act of one thing causing something
else to happen in some other part of the system.
An example of this is electromagnetic induction
(p.121), where a changing magnetic field (p.92)
causes an electromotive force (p.105).
induction (*n*).

transmit (*v*) to send from one place to another,
particularly radio waves (p.86). **transmission**
(*n*).

vibrate (*v*) to move forwards and backwards about a fixed position. **vibration** (*n*).

absorb

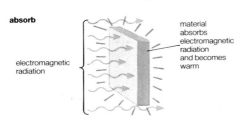

material absorbs electromagnetic radiation and becomes warm

electromagnetic radiation

porous

molecule of liquid or gas

porous material

absorb (*v*) to take in, particularly of energy in electromagnetic (p.115) radiation (p.241) which is usually turned into heat energy (p.18) in a material. **absorber** (*n*).

porous (*adj*) of a solid through which a liquid or a gas can pass, but only slowly. The molecules (p.188) that are passing through a porous material will not do so without hitting other molecules.

dissipate (*v*) to waste or destroy. It is particularly used of forms of energy which are changed to heat energy (p.18).

standard temperature and pressure a pressure (p.30) of 1.013×10^5 pascal (p.30) and a temperature (p.181) of 0°C. **s.t.p.** (*abbr*).

vacuum (*n*) a space which contains nothing, particularly no air.

evacuate (*v*) to take all the air out of a space.

screen[1] (*n*) an area on which a real image (p.64) is viewed, particularly a flat white surface from which light will be scattered in all directions.

screen[2] (*v*) to protect from some outside effect, e.g. electromagnetic (p.115) radiation (p.241).

signal (*n*) a quantity, usually a voltage (p.107) or current (p.103), used to carry some message, e.g. sound waves (p.42) turned into electrical signals by a microphone (p.58). Electrical signals can be turned back into sound waves by a loudspeaker (p.58).

amplifier (*n*) a circuit (p.104) into which a small signal (↑) is fed. The signal which comes out is larger but otherwise unchanged.

screen

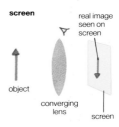

real image seen on screen

object

converging lens

screen

amplifier

amplifier

input

output

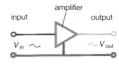

V_{in} ~

~ V_{out}

voltage

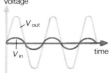

V_{out}

V_{in}

time

Index